ÆSOP'S FABLES

Æsop's Fables

BASED ON THE TRANSLATION OF
George Fyler Townsend

WITH AN INTRODUCTION BY

Isaac Bashevis Singer

Illustrated by MURRAY TINKELMAN

DOUBLEDAY & COMPANY, Inc.   Garden City, New York

CONTENTS

TABLE OF ILLUSTRATIONS

THE FABLE
AS LITERARY FORM

IN A TIME of literary verbosity and the writer's habit of burying images and events behind mountains of interpretation and analysis, it is a special pleasure to return to the brevity, directness, and clarity of the fable. Those who defined the fable—La Fontaine and Dr. Johnson—did not make a point of its conciseness, but took it for granted. And indeed although tales and allegories may be long, the fable is of its nature short. It is perhaps the oldest literary form, and probably already existed when man still lived in caves. It was also perhaps the first method of teaching both young and adult the wisdom of life in an entertaining manner.

There is proof that some of Æsop's fables have an earlier origin. In a sense the fable may have been the first fictional form. Ancient man believed that his tales and myths were true. But when it came to conversations between wolf and sheep, man and ape, fox and crow, bull and goat, even primitive man could not accept them as reality. A child understood that these stories were not to be taken as facts. The fable taught man that there is sometimes a deep truth behind an obvious falsehood. What is more, the fable was from the beginning, a worldly type of literature. When gods are mentioned in a fable they are not set apart or treated more seriously than other objects both animate and inanimate that are part of it.

The fable taught wisdom and morality mainly through the portrayal of character. In this sense as well, it represented a

basic element of fiction. One might say that the fable created
its own philosophy: the character of a being is its fate. Though
the wolf may speak sweetly, he remains a wolf with all his wolfish
attitudes and appetites. The fox remains sly. The cat always
persecutes mice. The lion is forever strong and majestic. The
fabulists knew that although circumstances play their part, they
cannot change nature. In no fable does the wolf become perma-
nently merciful, the cat a true friend of mice, or the hare be-
lievably courageous. It is a fact that the writers of fables used
clichés, but these were not clichés of style but symbols of eternal
character. The early writers of fiction knew instinctively that the
subject matter of literature is basic character that does not really
change with time and circumstances. Æsop's fables teach lessons both in life and literature that are valid today and will remain so forever. Thousands of years ago he pointed out that no
change in system can do away with the aggressor, the liar, the
flatterer, the intriguer, the exploiter, the parasite. Those Soviet
critics who complain bitterly today that Russian authors do not
portray the new nature of Soviet man have an object lesson in
Æsop's fables. If it were wise, Soviet censorship would ban
Æsop. He refuted Lysenko's theories many centuries before that
researcher was born. Æsop's fables mock all the illusions of the
"new man." His lions, wolves, foxes, and hares will outlive all
the social systems. Not only sociologists but pedagogues as well
may learn from Æsop.

As is always the case with true literature, Æsop's fables are
essentially pessimistic. Æsop does not offer humanity great
hopes. He realized long before Darwin that man is an animal
and that his ideals, motivations, and rationalizations are nothing
but a wolfish dialectic. When the human wolf finds no more ex-
cuses for eating the human sheep he says simply, "I'm hungry
and all your arguments will not fill my stomach." Nevertheless
in his fables Æsop does not belittle the importance of mutual
help. Since his animals are actually human characters, he often
adjusts the nature of the animal to that of man. Man may even

learn to be altruistic when he finally realizes that altruism can be made to suit his purposes.

Although characterology in the modern sense of the word is a new discipline, the study of human character and personality is one of the oldest of sciences. Ancient man had neither the means and perhaps not the curiosity to observe the behavior of animals too closely, but he early became a student of human nature. Æsop, despite the fact that he deals primarily with animals, owes his strength to his knowledge of humans. To portray mankind, Æsop makes his animals a lot more stupid than they actually are. No sheep will stop to argue with a wolf or believe in his promises. Such folly can only be committed by man, "the crown of creation." One sometimes has a feeling that Æsop in all his fables is saying: "If man were not so much more foolish and gullible than animals, he might have avoided a great deal of cruelty and misfortune."

Fables are not all of one kind, nor of one period. Such famous fabulists as La Fontaine, Lessing, and Krylov partially adjusted their fables to the epochs in which they lived. If Æsop were alive today he might have written a fable about a skunk who was psychoanalyzed to lose his stench, or about a hare who preached the dictatorship of hares. However, in essence, the fable remains the same. It is as constant as the types of human character. Art in general has much to learn from Æsop, because art as a reflection of human character can never undergo radical changes. When art begins to ape science it becomes exactly that —an ape. It appears just as ridiculous when it tries with its limited powers to retard or push forward the wheels of history.

There is no reason why some modern fabulist should not deal with jet planes, rockets, and in the not too distant future, even with animals that may exist on one of the planets. But he will never be able to escape from the age-old truths of Æsop.

ISAAC BASHEVIS SINGER

PREFACE

THE TALE, the Parable, and the Fable are all common and popular modes of conveying instruction. Each is distinguished by its own special characteristics. The Tale consists simply in the narration of a story either founded on facts, or created solely by the imagination, and not necessarily associated with the teaching of any moral lesson. The Parable is the designed use of language purposely intended to convey a hidden and secret meaning other than that contained in the words themselves; and which may or may not bear a special reference to the hearer, or reader. The Fable partly agrees with, and partly differs from both of these. It will contain, like the Tale, a short but real narrative; it will seek, like the Parable, to convey a hidden meaning, and that not so much by the use of language, as by the skilful introduction of fictitious characters; and yet unlike to either Tale or Parable, it will ever keep in view, as its high prerogative, and inseparable attribute, the great purpose of instruction, and will necessarily seek to inculcate some moral maxim, social duty, or political truth. The true Fable, if it rise to its high requirements, ever aims at one great end and purpose—the representation of human motive, and the improvement of human conduct, and yet it so conceals its design under the disguise of fictitious characters, by clothing with speech the animals of the field, the birds of the air, the trees of the wood, or the beasts of the forest, that the reader shall receive advice without perceiving the presence of the adviser. Thus the superiority of the counsellor, which often

25

renders counsel unpalatable, is kept out of view, and the lesson comes with the greater acceptance when the reader is led, unconsciously to himself, to have his sympathies enlisted in behalf of what is pure, honourable, and praiseworthy, and to have his indignation excited against what is low, ignoble, and unworthy. The true fabulist, therefore, discharges a most important function. He is neither a narrator, nor an allegorist. He is a great teacher, a corrector of morals, a censor of vice, and a commender of virtue. In this consists the superiority of the Fable over the Tale or the Parable. The fabulist is to create a laugh, but yet, under a merry guise, to convey instruction. Phædrus, the great imitator of Æsop, plainly indicates this double purpose to be the true office of the writer of fables.

> Duplex libelli dos est: quod risum movet,
> Et quod prudenti vitam consilio monet.

The continual observance of this twofold aim creates the charm, and accounts for the universal favour, of the fables of Æsop. "The fable," says Professor K. O. Mueller, "originated in Greece in an intentional travestie of human affairs. The 'ainos,' as its name denotes, is an admonition, or rather a reproof veiled, either from fear of an excess of frankness, or from a love of fun and jest, beneath the fiction of an occurrence happening among beasts; and wherever we have any ancient and authentic account of the Æsopian fables, we find it to be the same."[1]

The construction of a fable involves a minute attention to (1) the narration itself; (2) the deduction of the moral; and (3) a careful maintenance of the individual characteristics of the fictitious personages introduced into it. The narration should relate to one simple action, consistent with itself, and neither be overladen with a multiplicity of details, nor distracted by a variety of circumstances. The moral or lesson should be so plain, and so intimately interwoven with, and so necessarily dependent on, the narration, that every reader should be compelled to give to it the same undeniable interpretation. The introduction of the animals or fictitious characters should be marked with an unexceptionable care and attention to their natural attributes, and to the

qualities attributed to them by universal popular consent. The
Fox should be always cunning, the Hare timid, the Lion bold, the
Wolf cruel, the Bull strong, the Horse proud, and the Ass patient. Many of these fables are characterized by the strictest
observance of these rules. They are occupied with one short narrative, from which the moral naturally flows, and with which it
is intimately associated. " 'Tis the simple manner," says Dodsley,[2]
"in which the morals of Æsop are interwoven with his fables
that distinguishes him, and gives him the preference over all
other mythologists. His 'Mountain delivered of a Mouse,' pro-
duces the moral of his fable in ridicule of pompous pretenders;
and his Crow, when she drops her cheese, lets fall, as it were
by accident, the strongest admonition against the power of flat-
tery. There is no need of a separate sentence to explain it; no
possibility of impressing it deeper, by that load we too often see
of accumulated reflections."[3] An equal amount of praise is due
for the consistency with which the characters of the animals, fic-
titiously introduced, are marked. While they are made to depict
the motives and passions of men, they retain, in an eminent degree, their own special features of craft or counsel, of cowardice
or courage, of generosity or rapacity.

These terms of praise, it must be confessed, cannot be bestowed on all the fables in this collection. Many of them lack
that unity of design, that close connexion of the moral with the
narrative, that wise choice in the introduction of the animals,
which constitute the charm and excellency of true Æsopian
fable. This inferiority of some to others is sufficiently accounted
for in the history of the origin and descent of these fables. The
great bulk of them are not the immediate work of Æsop. Many
are obtained from ancient authors prior to the time in which he
lived. Thus, the fable of the "Hawk and the Nightingale" is related by Hesiod;[4] the "Eagle wounded by an Arrow, winged
with its own Feathers," by Æschylus;[5] the "Fox avenging his
wrongs on the Eagle," by Archilochus.[6] Many of them again are
of later origin, and are to be traced to the monks of the middle
ages: and yet this collection, though thus made up of fables both

earlier and later than the era of Æsop, rightfully bears his name, because he composed so large a number (all framed in the same mould, and conformed to the same fashion, and stamped with the same lineaments, image, and superscription) as to secure to himself the right to be considered the father of Greek fables, and the founder of this class of writing, which has ever since borne his name, and has secured for him, through all succeeding ages, the position of the first of moralists.[7]

The fables were in the first instance only narrated by Æsop, and for a long time were handed down by the uncertain channel of oral tradition. Socrates is mentioned by Plato[8] as having employed his time while in prison, awaiting the return of the sacred ship from Delphos which was to be the signal of his death, in turning some of these fables into verse, but he thus versified only such as he remembered. Demetrius Phalereus, a philosopher at Athens about 300 B.C., is said to have made the first collection of these fables. Phædrus, a slave by birth or by subsequent misfortunes, and admitted by Augustus to the honours of a freedman, imitated many of these fables in Latin iambics about the commencement of the Christian era. Aphthonius, a rhetorician of Antioch, A.C. 315, wrote a treatise on, and converted into Latin prose, some of these fables. This translation is the more worthy of notice, as it illustrates a custom of common use, both in these and in later times. The rhetoricians and philosophers were accustomed to give the Fables of Æsop as an exercise to their scholars, not only inviting them to discuss the moral of the tale, but also to practise and to perfect themselves thereby in style and rules of grammar, by making for themselves new and various versions of the fables. Ausonius,[9] the friend of the Emperor Valentinian, and the latest poet of eminence in the Western Empire, has handed down some of these fables in verse, which Julianus Titianus, a contemporary writer of no great name, translated into prose. Avienus, also a contemporary of Ausonius, put some of these fables into Latin elegiacs, which are given by Nevelet (in a book we shall refer to hereafter), and are occasionally incorporated with the editions of Phædrus.

Seven centuries elapsed before the next notice is found of the Fables of Æsop. During this long period these fables seem to have suffered an eclipse, to have disappeared and to have been forgotten; and it is at the commencement of the fourteenth century, when the Byzantine emperors were the great patrons of learning, and amidst the splendours of an Asiatic court, that we next find honours paid to the name and memory of Æsop. Maximus Planudes, a learned monk of Constantinople, made a collection of about a hundred and fifty of these fables. Little is known of his history. Planudes, however, was no mere recluse, shut up in his monastery. He took an active part in public affairs. In 1327 A.D. he was sent on a diplomatic mission to Venice by the Emperor Andronicus the Elder. This brought him into immediate contact with the Western Patriarch, whose interests he henceforth advocated with so much zeal as to bring on him suspicion and persecution from the rulers of the Eastern Church. Planudes has been exposed to a two-fold accusation. He is charged on the one hand with having had before him a copy of Babrias (to whom we shall have occasion to refer at greater length in the end of this Preface), and to have had the bad taste "to transpose," or to turn his poetical version into prose: and he is asserted, on the other hand, never to have seen the Fables of Æsop at all, but to have himself invented and made the fables which he palmed off under the name of the famous Greek fabulist. The truth lies between these two extremes. Planudes may have invented some few fables, or have inserted some that were current in his day; but there is an abundance of unanswerable internal evidence to prove that he had an acquaintance with the veritable fables of Æsop, although the versions he had access to were probably corrupt, as contained in the various translations and disquisitional exercises of the rhetoricians and philosophers. His collection is interesting and important, not only as the parent source or foundation of the earlier printed versions of Æsop, but as the direct channel of attracting to these fables the attention of the learned.

The eventual re-introduction, however, of these Fables of

Æsop to their high place in the general literature of Christen-
dom, is to be looked for in the West rather than in the East. The
calamities gradually thickening round the Eastern Empire, and
the fall of Constantinople, 1453 A.D. combined with other events
to promote the rapid restoration of learning in Italy; and with
that recovery of learning the revival of an interest in the Fables
of Æsop is closely identified. These fables, indeed, were
among the first writings of an earlier antiquity that attracted
attention. They took their place beside the Holy Scriptures and
the ancient classic authors, in the minds of the great students of
that day. Lorenzo Valla, one of the most famous promoters of
Italian learning, not only translated into Latin the Iliad of Homer
and the Histories of Herodotus and Thucydides, but also the
Fables of Æsop.

These fables, again, were among the books brought into an
extended circulation by the agency of the printing press. Bonus
Accursius, as early as 1475–1480, printed the collection of these
fables, made by Planudes, which, within five years afterwards,
Caxton translated into English, and printed at his press in West-
minster Abbey, 1485.[10] It must be mentioned also that the learning of this age has left permanent traces of its influence on
these fables,[11] by causing the interpolation with them (as a
κτῆμα εἰς ὄει) of some of those amusing stories which were so
frequently introduced into the public discourses of the great
preachers of those days, and of which specimens are yet to be
found in the extant sermons of Jean Raulin, Meffreth, and Ga-
briel Barlette.[12] The publication of this era which most probably
has influenced these fables, is the "Liber Facetiarum,"[13] a book
consisting of a hundred jests and stories, by the celebrated Poggio Bracciolini, published A.D. 1471, from which the two fables
of the "Miller, his Son, and the Ass," and the "Fox and the
Woodcutter," are undoubtedly selected.

The knowledge of these fables rapidly spread from Italy into
Germany, and their popularity was increased by the favour and
sanction given to them by the great fathers of the Reformation,
who frequently used them as vehicles for satire and protest

against the tricks and abuses of the Romish ecclesiastics. The zealous and renowned Camerarius, who took an active part in the preparation of the Confession of Augsburgh, found time, amidst his numerous avocations, to prepare a version for the students in the university of Tübingen, in which he was a professor. Martin Luther translated twenty of these fables, and was urged by Melancthon to complete the whole; while Gottfried Arnold, the celebrated Lutheran theologian, and librarian to Frederick I, king of Prussia, mentions that the great Reformer valued the Fables of Æsop next after the Holy Scriptures. In 1546 A.D. the second printed edition of the collection of the Fables made by Planudes, was issued from the printing-press of Robert Stephens, in which were inserted some additional fables from a MS. in the Bibliothêque du Roy at Paris.

The greatest advance, however, towards a re-introduction of the Fables of Æsop to a place in the literature of the world, was made in the early part of the seventeenth century. In the year 1610, a learned Swiss, Isaac Nicholas Nevelet, sent forth the third printed edition of these fables, in a work entitled "Mythologia Æsopica." This was a noble effort to do honour to the great fabulist, and was the most perfect collection of Æsopian fables ever yet published. It consisted, in addition to the collection of fables given by Planudes and reprinted in the various earlier editions, of one hundred and thirty-six new fables (never before published) from MSS. in the Library of the Vatican, of forty fables attributed to Aphthonius, and of forty-three from Babrias. It also contained the Latin versions of the same fables by Phædrus, Avienus, and other authors. This volume of Nevelet forms a complete "Corpus Fabularum Æsopicarum;" and to his labours Æsop owes his restoration to universal favour as one of the wise moralists and great teachers of mankind. During the interval of three centuries which has elapsed since the publication of this volume of Nevelet's, no book, with the exception of the Holy Scriptures, has had a wider circulation than Æsop's Fables. They have been translated into the greater number of the languages both of Europe and of the East, and have been read, and will be read, for generations, alike by Jew, Heathen, Mohammedan, and Christian. They are, at the present time, not only engrafted into the literature of the civilized world, but are familiar as household words in the common intercourse and daily conversation of the inhabitants of all countries.

This collection of Nevelet's is the great culminating point in the history of the revival of the fame and reputation of Æsopian Fables. It is remarkable, also, as containing in its preface the germ of an idea, which has been since proved to have been correct by a strange chain of circumstances. Nevelet intimates an opinion, that a writer named Babrias would be found to be the veritable author of the existing form of Æsopian Fables. This intimation has since given rise to a series of inquiries, the knowledge of which is necessary, in the present day, to a full understanding of the true position of Æsop in connexion with the writings that bear his name.

The history of Babrias is so strange and interesting, that it might not unfitly be enumerated among the curiosities of literature. He is generally supposed to have been a Greek of Asia Minor, of one of the Ionic Colonies, but the exact period in which he lived and wrote is yet unsettled. He is placed, by one critic,[14] as far back as the institution of the Achaian League, B.C. 250; by another as late as the Emperor Severus, who died A.D. 235; while others make him a contemporary with Phædrus in the time of Augustus. At whatever time he wrote his version of Æsop, by some strange accident it seems to have entirely disappeared, and to have been lost sight of. His name is mentioned by Avienus; by Suidas, a celebrated critic, at the close of the eleventh century, who gives in his lexicon several isolated verses of his version of the fables; and by John Tzetzes, a grammarian and poet of Constantinople, who lived during the latter half of the twelfth century. Nevelet, in the preface to the volume which we have described, points out that the Fables of Planudes could not be the work of Æsop, as they contain a reference in two places to "Holy monks," and give a verse from the Epistle of St. James as an "Epimith" to one of the fables, and suggests

Babrias as their author. Francis Vavassor,[15] a learned French jesuit, entered at greater length on this subject, and produced further proofs from internal evidence, from the use of the word Piræus in describing the harbour of Athens, a name which was not given till two hundred years after Æsop, and from the introduction of other modern words, that many of these fables must have been at least committed to writing posterior to the time of Æsop, and more boldly suggests Babrias as their author or collector.[16] These various references to Babrias induced Dr. Richard Bentley, at the close of the seventeenth century, to examine more minutely the existing versions of Æsop's Fables, and he maintained that many of them could, with a slight change of words, be resolved into the Scazonic[17] iambics, in which Babrias is known to have written: and, with a greater freedom than the evidence then justified, he put forth, in behalf of Babrias, a claim to the exclusive authorship of these fables. Such a seemingly extravagant theory, thus roundly asserted, excited much opposition. Dr. Bentley[18] met with an able antagonist in a member of the University of Oxford, the Hon. Mr. Charles Boyle,[19] afterwards Earl of Orrery. Their letters and disputations on this subject, enlivened on both sides with much wit and learning, will ever bear a conspicuous place in the literary history of the seventeenth century. The arguments of Dr. Bentley were yet further defended a few years later by Mr. Thomas Tyrwhitt, a well-read scholar, who gave up high civil distinctions that he might devote himself the more unreservedly to literary pursuits. Mr. Tyrwhitt published, A.D. 1776, a Dissertation on Babrias, and a collection of his fables in choliambic metre found in a MS. in the Bodleian Library at Oxford. Francesco de Furia, a learned Italian, contributed further testimony to the correctness of the supposition that Babrias had made a veritable collection of fables by printing from a MS. contained in the Vatican library several fables never before published. In the year 1844, however, new and unexpected light was thrown upon this subject. A veritable copy of Babrias was found in a manner as singular as were the MSS. of Quinctilian's Institutes, and of Cicero's Orations by

Poggio in the monastery of St. Gall A.D. 1416. M. Menoides, at the suggestion of M. Villemain, Minister of Public Instruction to King Louis Philippe, had been entrusted with a commission to search for ancient MSS., and in carrying out his instructions he found a MS. at the convent of St. Laura, on Mount Athos, which proved to be a copy of the long suspected and wished-for choliambic version of Babrias. This MS. was found to be divided into two books, the one containing a hundred and twenty-five, and the other ninety-five fables. This discovery attracted very general attention, not only as confirming, in a singular manner, the conjectures so boldly made by a long chain of critics, but as bringing to light valuable literary treasures tending to establish the reputation, and to confirm the antiquity and authenticity of the great mass of Æsopian Fable. The Fables thus recovered were soon published. They found a most worthy editor in the late distinguished Sir George Cornewall Lewis, and a translator equally qualified for his task, in the Reverend James Davies, M.A., sometime a scholar of Lincoln College, Oxford, and himself a relation of their English editor. Thus, after an eclipse of many centuries, Babrias shines out as the earliest, and most reliable collector of veritable Æsopian Fables.

* * * * *

The following are the sources from which the present translation has been prepared:—

Babrii Fabulæ Æsopeæ. George Cornewall Lewis. Oxford, 1846.

Babrii Fabulæ Æsopeæ. E codice manuscripto partem secundam edidit. George Cornewall Lewis. London: Parker, 1857.

Mythologica Æsopica. Opera et studia Isaaci Nicholai Neveleti. Frankfort, 1610.

Fabulæ Æsopiacæ, quales ante Planudem ferebantur cura et studio Francisci de Furia. Lipsiæ, 1810.

Αἰσωπείων Μυθῶν Συναγωγή. Ex recognitione Caroli Halmii. Lipsiæ, 1851.

Phædri Fabulæ Esopiæ. Delphin Classics. 1822.

GEORGE FYLER TOWNSEND

FOOTNOTES

[1] A History of the Literature of Ancient Greece, by K. O. Mueller. Vol. i, p. 191. *London*, Parker, 1858.

[2] Select Fables of Æsop, and other Fabulists. In three books, translated by Robert Dodsley, accompanied with a selection of notes, and an Essay on Fable.—*Birmingham*, 1864. P. 60.

[3] Some of these fables had, no doubt, in the first instance, a primary and private interpretation. On the first occasion of their being composed they were intended to refer to some passing event, or to some individual acts of wrong-doing. Thus, the fables of the "Eagle and the Fox" and of the "Fox and Monkey" are supposed to have been written by Archilochus, to avenge the injuries done him by Lycambes. So also the fables of the "Swollen Fox" and of the "Frogs asking a King" were spoken by Æsop for the immediate purpose of reconciling the inhabitants of Samos and Athens to their respective rulers, Periander and Pisistratus; while the fable of the "Horse and Stag" was composed to caution the inhabitants of Himera against granting a body-guard to Phalaris. In a similar manner, the fable from Phædrus, the "Marriage of the Sun," is supposed to have reference to the contemplated union of Livia, the daughter of Drusus, with Sejanus the favourite, and minister of Trajan. These fables, however, though thus originating in special events, and designed at first to meet special circumstances, are so admirably constructed as to be fraught with lessons of general utility, and of universal application.

[4] Hesiod. Opera et Dies, verse 202.

[5] Æschylus. Fragment of the Myrmidons. Æschylus speaks of this fable as existing before his day. See Scholiast on the Aves of Aristophanes, line 808.

[6] Fragment. 38, ed. Gaisford. See also Mueller's History of the Literature of Ancient Greece, vol. i. pp. 190–193.

[7] M. Bayle has well put this in his account of Æsop. "Il n'y a point d'apparence que les fables qui portent aujourd'hui son nom soient les mêmes qu'il avait faites; elles viennent bien de lui pour la plupart, quant à la

matière et la pensée; mais les paroles sont d'un autre." And again, "C'est donc à Hésiode, que j'aimerais mieux attribuer la gloire de l'invention; mais sans doute il laissa la chose très imparfaite. Esope la perfectionne si heureuse-ment, qu'on l'a regarde comme le vrai père de cette sorte de production."— *Bayle. Dictionnaire Historique.*

8 Plato in Phædone.

9 Apologos en! misit tibi
Ab usque Rheni limite
Ausonius nomen Italum
Præceptor Augusti tui
Æsopiam trimetriam;
Quam vertit exili stylo
Pedestre concinnans opus
Fandi Titianus artifex.
Ausonii Epistola, xvi. 75–80.

10 Both these publications are in the British Museum, and are placed in the library in cases under glass, for the inspection of the curious.

11 Fables may possibly have been not entirely unknown to the mediæval scholars. There are two celebrated works which might by some be classed amongst works of this description. The one is the "Speculum Sapientiæ," attributed to St. Cyril, Archbishop of Jerusalem, but of a considerably later origin, and existing only in Latin. It is divided into four books, and consists of long conversations conducted by fictitious characters under the figures of the beasts of the field and forest, and aimed at the rebuke of particular classes of men, the boastful, the proud, the luxurious, the wrathful, &c. None of the stories are precisely those of Æsop, and none have the concinnity, terseness, and unmistakeable deduction of the lesson intended to be taught by the fable, so conspicuous in the great Greek fabulist. The exact title of the book is this: "Speculum Sapientiæ, B. Cyrilli Episcopi: alias quadri-partitus apologeticus vocatus, in cujus quidem proverbiis omnis et totius sapientiæ speculum claret et feliciter incipit." The other is a larger work in two volumes, published in the fourteenth century by Cæsar Heisterbach, a Cistercian monk, under the title of "Dialogus Miraculorum," reprinted in 1851. This work consists of conversations in which many stories are inter-woven on all kinds of subjects. It has no correspondence with the pure Æsopian fable.

12 Post-mediæval Preachers, by S. Baring-Gould. Rivingtons, 1865.

13 For an account of this work see the Life of Poggio Bracciolini, by the Rev. William Shepherd. Liverpool. 1801.

14 Professor Theodore Bergh. See Classical Museum, No. viii. July, 1849.

15 Vavassor's treatise, entitled "De Ludicrâ Dictione" was written A.D. 1658, at the request of the celebrated M. Balzac (though published after his death), for the purpose of showing that the burlesque style of writing adopted by Scarron and D'Assouci, and at that time so popular in France, had no sanction from the ancient classic writers. *Francisci Vavassoris opera omnia.* Amsterdam, 1709.

[16] The claims of Babrias also found a warm advocate in the learned Frenchman, M. Bayle, who, in his admirable Dictionary, (*Dictionnaire Historique et Critique de Pierre Bayle*. Paris, 1820,) gives additional arguments in confirmation of the opinions of his learned predecessors, Nevelet and Vavassor.

[17] Scazonic, or halting, iambics; a choliambic (a lame, halting iambic) differs from the iambic Senarius in always having a spondee or trochee for its last foot; the fifth foot, to avoid shortness of metre, being generally an iambic. See Fables of Babrias, translated by Rev. James Davies. Lockwood, 1860. Preface, p. 27.

[18] See Dr. Bentley's Dissertations upon the Epistles of Phalaris.

[19] Dr. Bentley's Dissertations on the Epistles of Phalaris, and Fables of Æsop examined. By the Honourable Charles Boyle.

EDITORS' NOTE: In the *Preface* and *Life of Æsop*, the wording, spelling, and punctuation have been left exactly as George Fyler Townsend originally set them down. However, minor editorial changes have been made in the fables themselves to clarify archaic wording and usage.

ÆSOP'S FABLES

The Wolf and the Lamb

A WOLF, meeting with a Lamb astray from the fold, resolved not to lay violent hands on him, but to find some plea to justify to the Lamb the Wolf's right to eat him. He thus addressed him: "Sirrah, last year you grossly insulted me." "Indeed," bleated the Lamb in a mournful tone of voice, "I was not then born." Then said the Wolf, "You feed in my pasture." "No, good sir," replied the Lamb, "I have not yet tasted grass." Again said the Wolf, "You drink of my well." "No," exclaimed the Lamb, "I never yet drank water, for as yet my mother's milk is both food and drink to me." Upon which the Wolf seized him and ate him up, saying, "Well! I won't remain supperless, even though you refute every one of my imputations."

The tyrant will always find a pretext for his tyranny.

The Bat and the Weasels

A BAT who fell upon the ground and was caught by a Weasel pleaded to be spared his life. The Weasel refused, saying that he was by nature the enemy of all birds. The Bat assured him that he was not a bird, but a mouse, and thus was set free. Shortly afterwards the Bat again fell to the ground and was caught by another Weasel, whom he likewise entreated not to eat him. The Weasel said that he had a special hostility to mice. The Bat assured him that he was not a mouse, but a bat, and thus a second time escaped.

It is wise to turn circumstances to good account.

The Ass and the Grasshopper

AN ASS having heard some Grasshoppers chirping, was highly enchanted; and, desiring to possess the same charms of melody, demanded what sort of food they lived on to give them such beautiful voices. They replied, "The dew." The Ass resolved that he would live only upon dew, and in a short time died of hunger.

The Lion and the Mouse

A LION was awakened from sleep by a Mouse running over his face. Rising up angrily, he caught him and was about to kill him, when the Mouse piteously entreated, saying: "If you would only spare my life, I would be sure to repay your kindness." The Lion laughed and let him go. It happened shortly after this that the Lion was caught by some hunters, who bound him by strong ropes to the ground. The Mouse, recognizing his roar, came up, gnawed the rope with his teeth, and set him free, exclaiming:

"You ridiculed the idea of my ever being able to help you, not expecting to receive from me any repayment of your favor; but now you know that it is possible for even a Mouse to confer benefits on a Lion."

The Charcoal-Burner and the Fuller

A CHARCOAL-BURNER carried on his trade in his own house. One day he met a friend, a Fuller, and entreated him to come and live with him, saying that they should be far better neighbors and that their housekeeping expenses would be lessened. The Fuller replied, "The arrangement is impossible as far as I am concerned, for whatever I should whiten, you would immediately blacken again with your charcoal."

Like will draw like.

The Father and His Sons

A FATHER had a family of sons who were perpetually quarreling among themselves. When he failed to heal their disputes by his exhortations, he determined to give them a practical illustration of the evils of disunion; and for this purpose he one day told them to bring him a bundle of sticks. When they had done so, he placed the faggot into the hands of each of them in succession, and ordered them to break it in pieces. They tried with all their strength, and were not able to do it. He next opened the faggot, took the sticks separately, one by one, and again put them into his sons' hands, upon which they broke them easily. He then addressed them in these words: "My sons, if you are of one mind, and unite to assist each other, you will be as this faggot, uninjured by all the attempts of your enemies; but if you are divided among yourselves, you will be broken as easily as these sticks."

The Boy Hunting Locusts

A BOY was hunting for locusts. He had caught a goodly number, when he saw a Scorpion, and mistaking him for a locust, reached out his hand to take him. The Scorpion, showing his sting, said: "If you had but touched me, my friend, you would have lost me, and all your locusts too!"

The Cock and the Jewel

A COCK, scratching for food for himself and his hens, found a precious stone and exclaimed: "If your owner had found thee, and not I, he would have taken thee up, and have set thee in thy first estate; but I have found thee for no purpose. I would rather have one barleycorn than all the jewels in the world."

The Kingdom of the Lion

THE BEASTS of the field and forest had a Lion as their king. He was neither wrathful, cruel, nor tyrannical, but just and gentle as a king could be. During his reign he made a royal proclamation for a general assembly of all the birds and beasts, and drew up conditions for a universal league, in which the Wolf and the Lamb, the Panther and the Kid, the Tiger and the Stag, the Dog and the Hare, should live together in perfect peace and amity. The Hare said, "Oh, how I have longed to see this day, in which the weak shall take their place with impunity by the side of the strong." And after the Hare said this, he ran for his life.

The Wolf and the Crane

A WOLF who had a bone stuck in his throat hired a Crane, for a large sum, to put her head into his mouth and draw out the bone. When the Crane had extracted the bone and demanded the promised payment, the Wolf, grinning and grinding his teeth, exclaimed: "Why, you have surely already had a sufficient recompense, in having been permitted to draw out your head in safety from the mouth and jaws of a wolf."

In serving the wicked, expect no reward, and be thankful if you escape injury for your pains.

The Fisherman Piping

A FISHERMAN skilled in music took his flute and his nets to the seashore. Standing on a projecting rock, he played several tunes in the hope that the fish, attracted by his melody, would of their own accord dance into his net, which he had placed below. At last, having long waited in vain, he laid aside his flute, and casting his net into the sea, made an excellent haul of fish. When he saw them leaping about in the net upon the rock he said: "O you most perverse creatures, when I piped you would not dance, but now that I have ceased you do so merrily."

Hercules and the Wagoner

A CARTER was driving a wagon along a country lane, when the wheels sank down deep into a rut. The rustic driver, stupified and aghast, stood looking at the wagon, and did nothing but utter loud cries to Hercules to come and help him. Hercules, it is said, appeared and thus addressed him: "Put your shoulders to the wheels, my man. Goad on your bullocks, and never more pray to me for help, until you have done your best to help yourself, or depend upon it you will henceforth pray in vain."

Self-help is the best help.

The Ants and the Grasshopper

THE ANTS were spending a fine winter's day drying grain collected in the summertime. A Grasshopper, perishing with famine, passed by and earnestly begged for a little food. The Ants inquired of him, "Why did you not treasure up food during the summer?" He replied, "I had not leisure enough. I passed the days in singing." They then said in derision: "If you were foolish enough to sing all the summer, you must dance supperless to bed in the winter."

The Traveler and His Dog

A TRAVELER about to set out on a journey saw his Dog stand at the door stretching himself. He asked him sharply: "Why do you stand there gaping? Everything is ready but you, so come with me instantly." The Dog, wagging his tail, replied: "O, master! I am quite ready; it is you for whom I am waiting."

The loiterer often blames delay on his more active friend.

The Dog and the Shadow

A DOG, crossing a bridge over a stream with a piece of flesh in his mouth, saw his own shadow in the water and took it for that of another Dog, with a piece of meat double his own in size. He immediately let go of his own, and fiercely attacked the other Dog to get his larger piece from him. He thus lost both: that which he grasped at in the water, because it was a shadow; and his own, because the stream swept it away.

The Mole and His Mother

A MOLE, a creature blind from birth, once said to his Mother: "I am sure that I can see, Mother!" In the desire to prove to him his mistake, his Mother placed before him a few grains of frankincense, and asked, "What is it?" The young Mole said, "It is a pebble." His Mother exclaimed: "My son, I am afraid that you are not only blind, but that you have lost your sense of smell."

The Herdsman and the Lost Bull

A HERDSMAN tending his flock in a forest lost a Bull-calf from the fold. After a long and fruitless search, he made a vow that, if he could only discover the thief who had stolen the Calf, he would offer a lamb in sacrifice to Hermes, Pan, and the Guardian Deities of the forest. Not long afterwards, as he ascended a small hillock, he saw at its foot a Lion feeding on the Calf. Terrified at the sight, he lifted his eyes and his hands to heaven, and said: "Just now I vowed to offer a lamb to the Guardian Deities of the forest if I could only find out who had robbed me; but now that I have discovered the thief, I would willingly add a full-grown Bull to the Calf I have lost, if I may only secure my own escape from him in safety."

The Hare and the Tortoise

A HARE one day ridiculed the short feet and slow pace of the Tortoise, who replied, laughing: "Though you be swift as the wind, I will beat you in a race." The Hare, believing her assertion to be simply impossible, assented to the proposal; and they agreed that the Fox should choose the course and fix the goal. On the day appointed for the race the two started together. The Tortoise never for a moment stopped, but went on with a slow but steady pace straight to the end of the course. The Hare, trusting to his native swiftness, cared little about the race, and lying down by the wayside, fell fast asleep. At last waking up, and moving as fast as he could, he saw the Tortoise had reached the goal, and was comfortably dozing after her fatigue.

Slow but steady wins the race.

The Pomegranate, Apple-Tree, and Bramble

THE POMEGRANATE and Apple-Tree disputed as to which was the most beautiful. When their strife was at its height, a Bramble from the neighboring hedge lifted up its voice, and said in a boastful tone: "Pray, my dear friends, in my presence at least cease from such vain disputings."

The Farmer and the Stork

A FARMER placed nets on his newly-sown plowlands and caught a number of Cranes, which came to pick up his seed. With them he trapped a Stork that had fractured his leg in the net and was earnestly beseeching the Farmer to spare his life. "Pray save me, Master," he said, "and let me go free this once. My broken limb should excite your pity. Besides, I am no Crane, I am a Stork, a bird of excellent character; and see how I love and slave for my father and mother. Look too, at my feathers— they are not the least like those of a Crane." The Farmer laughed aloud and said, "It may be all as you say, I only know this: I have taken you with these robbers, the Cranes, and you must die in their company."

Birds of a feather flock together.

The Farmer and the Snake

ONE WINTER a Farmer found a Snake stiff and frozen with cold. He had compassion on it, and taking it up, placed it in his bosom. The Snake was quickly revived by the warmth, and resuming its natural instincts, bit its benefactor, inflicting on him a mortal wound. "Oh," cried the Farmer with his last breath, "I am rightly served for pitying a scoundrel."

The greatest kindness will not bind the ungrateful.

The Fawn and His Mother

A YOUNG FAWN once said to his Mother, "You are larger than a dog, and swifter, and more used to running, and you have your horns as a defense; why, then, O Mother! do the hounds frighten you so?" She smiled, and said: "I know full well, my son, that all you say is true. I have the advantages you mention, but when I hear even the bark of a single dog I feel ready to faint, and fly away as fast as I can."

No arguments will give courage to the coward.

The Bear and the Fox

A BEAR boasted very much of his philanthropy, saying that of all animals he was the most tender in his regard for man, for he had such respect for him that he would not even touch his dead body. A Fox hearing these words said with a smile to the Bear, "Oh! that you would eat the dead and not the living."

The Swallow and the Crow

THE SWALLOW and the Crow had a contention about their plumage. The Crow put an end to the dispute by saying, "Your feathers are all very well in the spring, but mine protect me against the winter."

Fair weather friends are not worth much.

The Mountain in Labor

A MOUNTAIN was once greatly agitated. Loud groans and noises were heard, and crowds of people came from all parts to see what was the matter. While they were assembled in anxious expectation of some terrible calamity, out came a Mouse.

Don't make much ado about nothing.

The Ass, the Fox, and the Lion

THE ASS and the Fox, having entered into partnership together for their mutual protection, went out into the forest to hunt. They had not proceeded far when they met a Lion. The Fox, seeing imminent danger, approached the Lion and promised to contrive for him the capture of the Ass if the Lion would pledge his word not to harm the Fox. Then, upon assuring the Ass that he would not be injured, the Fox led him to a deep pit and arranged that he should fall into it. The Lion, seeing that the Ass was secured, immediately clutched the Fox, and attacked the Ass at his leisure.

The Tortoise and the Eagle

A TORTOISE, lazily basking in the sun, complained to the sea-birds of her hard fate, that no one would teach her to fly. An Eagle, hovering near, heard her lamentation and demanded what reward she would give him if he would take her aloft and float her in the air. "I will give you," she said, "all the riches of the Red Sea." "I will teach you to fly then," said the Eagle; and taking her up in his talons he carried her almost to the clouds—when suddenly he let her go, and she fell on a lofty mountain, dashing her shell to pieces. The Tortoise exclaimed in the moment of death: "I have deserved my present fate; for what had I to do with wings and clouds, who can with difficulty move about on the earth?"

If men had all they wished, they would be often ruined.

The Flies and the Honey-Pot

A NUMBER of Flies were attracted to a jar of honey which had been overturned in a housekeeper's room, and placing their feet in it, ate greedily. Their feet, however, became so smeared with the honey that they could not use their wings, nor release themselves, and were suffocated. Just as they were expiring, they exclaimed, "O foolish creatures that we are, for the sake of a little pleasure we have destroyed ourselves."

Pleasure bought with pains, hurts.

The Man and the Lion

A MAN and a Lion traveled together through the forest. They soon began to boast of their respective superiority to each other in strength and prowess. As they were disputing, they passed a statue carved in stone, which represented "a Lion strangled by a Man." The traveler pointed to it and said: "See there! How strong we are, and how we prevail over even the king of beasts." The Lion replied: "This statue was made by one of you men. If we Lions knew how to erect statues, you would see the Man placed under the paw of the Lion."

One story is good, till another is told.

The Farmer and the Cranes

SOME CRANES made their feeding grounds on some plowlands newly sown with wheat. For a long time the Farmer, brandishing an empty sling, chased them away by the terror he inspired; but when the birds found that the sling was only swung in the air, they ceased to take any notice of it and would not move. The Farmer, on seeing this, charged his sling with stones, and killed a great number. The remaining birds at once forsook his fields, crying to each other, "It is time for us to be off to Liliput: for this man is no longer content to scare us, but begins to show us in earnest what he can do."

If words suffice not, blows must follow.

The Dog in the Manger

A DOG lay in a manger, and by his growling and snapping prevented the oxen from eating the hay which had been placed for them. "What a selfish Dog!" said one of them to his companions; "he cannot eat the hay himself, and yet refuses to allow those to eat who can."

The Fox and the Goat

A FOX one day fell into a deep well and could find no means of escape. A Goat, overcome with thirst, came to the same well, and seeing the Fox, inquired if the water was good. Concealing his sad plight under a merry guise, the Fox indulged in a lavish praise of the water, saying it was excellent beyond measure, and encouraging him to descend. The Goat, mindful only of his

thirst, thoughtlessly jumped down, but just as he drank, the Fox informed him of the difficulty they were both in and suggested a scheme for their common escape. "If," said he, "you will place your forefeet upon the wall and bend your head, I will run up your back and escape, and will help you out afterwards." The Goat readily assented and the Fox leaped upon his back. Steadying himself with the Goat's horns, he safely reached the mouth of the well and made off as fast as he could. When the Goat upbraided him for breaking his promise, he turned around and cried out, "You foolish old fellow! If you had as many brains in your head as you have hairs in your beard, you would never have gone down before you had inspected the way up, nor have exposed yourself to dangers from which you had no means of escape."

Look before you leap.

The Bear and the Two Travelers

TWO MEN were traveling together, when a Bear suddenly met them on their path. One of them climbed up quickly into a tree and concealed himself in the branches. The other, seeing that he must be attacked, fell flat on the ground, and when the Bear came up and felt him with his snout, and smelt him all over, he held his breath, and feigned the appearance of death as much as he could. The Bear soon left him, for it is said he will not touch a dead body. When he was quite gone, the other Traveler descended from the tree, and jocularly inquired of his friend what it was the Bear had whispered in his ear. "He gave me this advice," his companion replied. "Never travel with a friend who deserts you at the approach of danger."

Misfortune tests the sincerity of friends.

The Oxen and the Axle-Trees

A HEAVY WAGON was being dragged along a country lane by a team of Oxen. The Axle-trees groaned and creaked terribly; whereupon the Oxen, turning round, thus addressed the wheels: "Hullo there! why do you make so much noise? We bear all the labor, and we, not you, ought to cry out."

Those who suffer most cry out the least.

The Thirsty Pigeon

A PIGEON, oppressed by excessive thirst, saw a goblet of water painted on a signboard. Not supposing it to be only a picture, she flew towards it with a loud whirr and unwittingly dashed against the signboard, jarring herself terribly. Having broken her wings by the blow, she fell to the ground, and was caught by one of the bystanders.

Zeal should not outrun discretion.

The Raven and the Swan

A RAVEN saw a Swan and desired to secure for himself the same beautiful plumage. Supposing that the Swan's splendid white color arose from his washing in the water in which he swam, the

Raven left the altars in the neighborhood where he picked up his living, and took up residence in the lakes and pools. But cleansing his feathers as often as he would, he could not change their color, while through want of food he perished.

Change of habit cannot alter Nature.

The Goat and the Goatherd

A GOATHERD had sought to bring back a stray goat to his flock. He whistled and sounded his horn in vain; the straggler paid no attention to the summons. At last the Goatherd threw a stone, and breaking its horn, begged the Goat not to tell his master. The Goat replied, "Why, you silly fellow, the horn will speak though I be silent."

Do not attempt to hide things which cannot be hid.

The Miser

A MISER sold all that he had and bought a lump of gold, which he buried in a hole in the ground by the side of an old wall and went to look at daily. One of his workmen observed his frequent visits to the spot and decided to watch his movements. He soon discovered the secret of the hidden treasure, and digging down, came to the lump of gold, and stole it. The Miser, on his next visit, found the hole empty and began to tear his hair and to make loud lamentations. A neighbor, seeing him overcome with grief and learning the cause, said, "Pray do not grieve so; but go and take a stone, and place it in the hole, and fancy that the gold is still lying there. It will do you quite the same service; for when the gold was there, you had it not, as you did not make the slightest use of it."

The Sick Lion

A LION, unable from old age and infirmities to provide himself with food by force, resolved to do so by artifice. He returned to his den, and lying down there, pretended to be sick, taking care that his sickness should be publicly known. The beasts expressed their sorrow, and came one by one to his den, where the Lion devoured them. After many of the beasts had thus disappeared, the Fox discovered the trick, and presenting himself to the Lion, stood on the outside of the cave, at a respectful distance, and asked him how he was. "I am very middling," replied the Lion, "but why do you stand without? Pray enter within to talk with me." "No, thank you," said the Fox. "I notice that there are many prints of feet entering your cave, but I see no trace of any returning."

He is wise who is warned by the misfortunes of others.

The Horse and Groom

A GROOM used to spend whole days in currycombing and rubbing down his Horse, but at the same time stole his oats and sold them for his own profit. "Alas!" said the Horse, "if you really wish me to be in good condition, you should groom me less, and feed me more."

The Ass and the Lapdog

A MAN had an Ass, and a Maltese Lapdog, a very great beauty. The Ass was left in a stable and had plenty of oats and hay to eat, just as any other Ass would. The Lapdog knew many tricks and was a great favorite with his master, who often fondled him and seldom went out to dine without bringing him home some tidbit to eat. The Ass, on the contrary, had much work to do in grinding the corn-mill and in carrying wood from the forest or burdens from the farm. He often lamented his own hard fate and contrasted it with the luxury and idleness of the Lapdog, till at last one day he broke his cords and halter, and galloped into his master's house, kicking up his heels without measure, and frisking and fawning as well as he could. He next tried to jump about his master as he had seen the Lapdog do, but he broke the table and smashed all the dishes upon it to atoms. He then attempted to lick his master, and jumped upon his back. The servants, hearing the strange hubbub and perceiving the danger of their master, quickly relieved him, and drove out the Ass to his stable with kicks and clubs and cuffs. The Ass, as he returned to his stall beaten nearly to death, thus lamented: "I have brought it all on myself! Why could I not have been contented to labor with my companions, and not wish to be idle all the day like that useless little Lapdog!"

The Lioness

A CONTROVERSY prevailed among the beasts of the field as to which of the animals deserved the most credit for producing the greatest number of whelps at a birth. They rushed clamorously into the presence of the Lioness and demanded of her the settlement of the dispute. "And you," they said, "how many sons have you at a birth?" The Lioness laughed at them, and said: "Why! I have only one; but that one is altogether a thoroughbred Lion."

The value is in the worth, not in the number.

The Boasting Traveler

A MAN who had traveled in foreign lands boasted very much, on returning to his own country, of the many wonderful and heroic feats he had performed in the different places he had visited. Among other things, he said that when he was at Rhodes he had leaped to such a distance that no man of his day could leap anywhere near him—and as to that, there were in Rhodes many persons who saw him do it and whom he could call as witnesses. One of the bystanders interrupted him, saying: "Now, my good man, if this be all true there is no need of witnesses. Suppose this to be Rhodes, and leap for us."

The Cat and the Cock

A CAT caught a Cock, and pondered how he might find a reasonable excuse for eating him. He accused him of being a nuisance to men by crowing in the nighttime and not permitting them to sleep. The Cock defended himself by saying that he did this for the benefit of men, that they might rise in time for their labors. The Cat replied, "Although you abound in specious apologies, I shall not remain supperless"; and he made a meal of him.

The Lion in Love

A LION demanded the daughter of a woodcutter in marriage. The Father, unwilling to grant, and yet afraid to refuse his request, hit upon this expedient to rid himself of his importunities. He expressed his willingness to accept the Lion as the suitor of his daughter on one condition: that he should allow him to extract his teeth, and cut off his claws, as his daughter was fearfully afraid of both. The Lion cheerfully assented to the proposal. But when the toothless, clawless Lion returned to repeat his request, the Woodman, no longer afraid, set upon him with his club, and drove him away into the forest.

The Piglet, the Sheep, and the Goat

A YOUNG PIG was shut up in a fold-yard with a Goat and a Sheep. On one occasion when the shepherd laid hold of him, he grunted and squeaked and resisted violently. The Sheep and the Goat complained of his distressing cries, saying, "He often handles us, and we do not cry out." To this the Pig replied, "Your handling and mine are very different things. He catches you only for your wool, or your milk, but he lays hold on me for my very life."

The Boy and the Filberts

A BOY put his hand into a pitcher full of filberts. He grasped as many as he could possibly hold, but when he tried to pull out his hand, he was prevented from doing so by the neck of the pitcher. Unwilling to lose his filberts, and yet unable to withdraw his hand, he burst into tears and bitterly lamented his disappointment. A bystander said to him, "Be satisfied with half the quantity, and you will readily draw out your hand."

Do not attempt too much at once.

The Laborer and the Snake

A SNAKE, having made his hole close to the porch of a cottage, inflicted a mortal bite on the Cottager's infant son. Grieving over his loss, the Father resolved to kill the Snake. The next day, when it came out of its hole for food, he took up his axe, but by swinging too hastily, missed its head and cut off only the end of its tail. After some time the Cottager, afraid that the Snake would bite him also, endeavored to make peace, and placed some bread and salt in the hole. The Snake, slightly hissing, said: "There can henceforth be no peace between us; for whenever I see you I shall remember the loss of my tail, and whenever you see me you will be thinking of the death of your son."

No one truly forgets injuries in the presence of him who caused the injury.

The Wolf in Sheep's Clothing

ONCE UPON A TIME a Wolf resolved to disguise his appearance in order to secure food more easily. Encased in the skin of a sheep, he pastured with the flock, deceiving the shepherd by his costume. In the evening he was shut up by the shepherd in the fold; the gate was closed, and the entrance made thoroughly secure. But the shepherd, returning to the fold during the night to obtain meat for the next day, mistakenly caught up the Wolf instead of a sheep, and killed him instantly.

Harm seek, harm find.

The Ass and the Mule

A MULETEER set forth on a journey, driving before him an Ass and a Mule, both well laden. The Ass, as long as he traveled along the plain, carried his load with ease, but when he began to ascend the steep path of the mountain, felt his load to be more than he could bear. He entreated his companion to relieve him of a small portion, that he might carry home the rest; but the Mule paid no attention to the request. The Ass shortly afterwards fell down dead under his burden. Not knowing what else to do in so wild a region, the Muleteer placed upon the Mule the load carried by the Ass in addition to his own, and at the top of all placed the hide of the Ass, after he had skinned him. The Mule, groaning beneath his heavy burden, said to himself: "I am treated according to my deserts. If I had only been willing to assist the Ass a little in his need, I should not now be bearing, together with his burden, himself as well."

The Frogs Asking for a King

THE FROGS, grieved at having no established Ruler, sent ambassadors to Jupiter entreating for a King. Perceiving their simplicity, he cast down a huge log into the lake. The Frogs were terrified at the splash occasioned by its fall and hid themselves in the depths of the pool. But as soon as they realized that the huge log was motionless, they swam again to the top of the water, dismissed their fears, climbed up, and began squatting on it in contempt. After some time they began to think themselves ill-treated in the appointment of so inert a Ruler, and sent a second deputation to Jupiter to pray that he would set over them another sovereign. He then gave them an Eel to govern them. When the Frogs discovered his easy good nature, they sent yet a third time to Jupiter to beg him to choose for them still another King. Jupiter, displeased with all their complaints, sent a Heron, who preyed upon the Frogs day by day till there were none left to croak upon the lake.

The Boys and the Frogs

SOME BOYS, playing near a pond, saw a number of Frogs in the water and began to pelt them with stones. They killed several of them, when one of the Frogs, lifting his head out of the water, cried out: "Pray stop, my boys: what is sport to you, is death to us."

The Sick Stag

A SICK STAG lay down in a quiet corner of its pasture-ground. His companions came in great numbers to inquire after his health, and each one helped himself to a share of the food which had been placed for his use; so that he died, not from his sickness, but from the failure of the means of living.

Evil companions bring more hurt than profit.

The Salt Merchant and His Ass

A PEDDLER drove his Ass to the seashore to buy salt. His road home lay across a stream into which his Ass, making a false step, fell by accident and rose up again with his load considerably lighter, as the water melted the salt. The Peddler retraced his steps and refilled his panniers with a larger quantity of salt than before. When he came again to the stream, the Ass fell down on purpose in the same spot, and, regaining his feet with the weight of his load much diminished, brayed triumphantly as if he had obtained what he desired. The Peddler saw through his trick and drove him for the third time to the coast, where he bought a cargo of sponges instead of salt. The Ass, again playing the fool, fell down on purpose when he reached the stream, but the sponges became swollen with water, greatly increasing his load. And thus his trick recoiled on him, for he now carried on his back a double burden.

The Oxen and the Butchers

THE OXEN once upon a time sought to destroy the Butchers, who practiced a trade destructive to their race. They assembled on a certain day to carry out their purpose, and sharpened their horns for the contest. But one of them who was exceedingly old (for many a field had he plowed) thus spoke: "These Butchers, it is true, slaughter us, but they do so with skillful hands, and with no unnecessary pain. If we get rid of them, we shall fall into the hands of unskillful operators, and thus suffer a double death: for you may be assured, that though all the Butchers should perish, yet will men never want beef."

Do not be in a hurry to change one evil for another.

The Lion, the Mouse, and the Fox

A LION, fatigued by the heat of a summer's day, fell fast asleep in his den. A Mouse ran over his mane and ears and woke him from his slumbers. He rose up and shook himself in great wrath, and searched every corner of his den to find the Mouse. A Fox seeing him said: "A fine Lion you are, to be frightened of a Mouse." "'Tis not the Mouse I fear," said the Lion; "I resent his familiarity and ill-breeding."

Little liberties are great offenses.

The Vain Jackdaw

JUPITER DETERMINED, it is said, to create a sovereign over the birds, and made proclamation that on a certain day they should all present themselves before him, when he would himself choose the most beautiful among them to be king. The Jackdaw, knowing his own ugliness, searched through the woods and fields, and collected the feathers which had fallen from the wings of his companions, and stuck them in all parts of his body, hoping thereby to make himself the most beautiful of all. When the appointed day arrived, and the birds had assembled before Jupiter, the Jackdaw also made his appearance in his many-feathered finery. But when Jupiter proposed to make him king because of the beauty of his plumage, the birds indignantly protested, and each plucked from him his own feathers, leaving the Jackdaw nothing but a Jackdaw.

The Goatherd and the Wild Goats

A GOATHERD, driving his flock from their pasture at eventide, found some Wild Goats mingled among them, and shut them up together with his own for the night. The next day it snowed very hard, so that he could not take the herd to their usual feeding-places, but was obliged to keep them in the fold. He gave his own goats just sufficient food to keep them alive, but fed the strangers more abundantly in the hope of enticing them to stay with him and of making them his own. When the thaw set in, he led them all out to feed, and the Wild Goats scampered away as fast as they could to the mountains. The Goatherd scolded them for their ingratitude in leaving him, when during the storm he had taken more care of them than of his own herd. One of them, turning about, said to him: "That is the very reason why we are so cautious; for if you yesterday treated us better than the Goats you have had so long, it is plain also that if others came after us, you would in the same manner prefer them to ourselves."

Old friends cannot with impunity be sacrificed for new ones.

The Mischievous Dog

A DOG used to run up quietly to the heels of everyone he met, and to bite them without notice. His master suspended a bell about his neck so that the Dog might give notice of his presence wherever he went. Thinking it a mark of distinction, the Dog grew proud of his bell and went tinkling it all over the market-place. One day an old hound said to him: "Why do you make such an exhibition of yourself? That bell that you carry is not, believe me, any order of merit, but on the contrary a mark of disgrace, a public notice to all men to avoid you as an ill-mannered dog."

Notoriety is often mistaken for fame.

The Fox Who Had Lost His Tail

A FOX caught in a trap escaped, but in so doing lost his tail. Thereafter, feeling his life a burden from the shame and ridicule to which he was exposed, he schemed to convince all the other Foxes that being tailless was much more attractive, thus making up for his own deprivation. He assembled a good many Foxes and publicly advised them to cut off their tails, saying that they would not only look much better without them, but that they would get rid of the weight of the brush, which was a very great inconvenience. One of them interrupting him said, "If you had not yourself lost your tail, my friend, you would not thus counsel us."

The Boy and the Nettles

A BOY was stung by a Nettle. He ran home and told his Mother, saying, "Although it hurts me very much, I only touched it gently." "That was just why it stung you," said his Mother. "The next time you touch a Nettle, grasp it boldly, and it will be soft as silk to your hand, and not in the least hurt you."

Whatever you do, do with all your might.

The Man and His Two Sweethearts

A MIDDLE-AGED MAN, whose hair had begun to turn gray, courted two women at the same time. One of them was young, and the other well advanced in years. The elder woman, ashamed to be courted by a man younger than herself, made a point, whenever her admirer visited her, to pull out some portion of his black hairs. The younger, on the contrary, not wishing to become the wife of an old man, was equally zealous in removing every gray hair she could find. Thus it came to pass that between them both he very soon found that he had not a hair left on his head.

Those who seek to please everybody please nobody.

The Astronomer

AN ASTRONOMER used to go out at night to observe the stars. One evening, as he wandered through the suburbs with his whole attention fixed on the sky, he fell accidentally into a deep well. While he lamented and bewailed his sores and bruises, and cried loudly for help, a neighbor ran to the well, and learning what had happened said: "Hark ye, old fellow, why, in striving to pry into what is in heaven, do you not manage to see what is on earth?"

The Wolves and the Sheep

"WHY SHOULD there always be this fear and slaughter between us?" said the Wolves to the Sheep. "Those evil-disposed Dogs have much to answer for. They always bark whenever we approach you and attack us before we have done any harm. If you would only dismiss them from your heels, there might soon be treaties of peace and reconciliation between us." The Sheep, poor silly creatures! were easily beguiled and dismissed the Dogs, whereupon the Wolves destroyed the unguarded flock at their own pleasure.

The Old Woman and the Physician

AN OLD WOMAN having lost the use of her eyes, called in a Physician to heal them, and made this bargain with him in the presence of witnesses: that if he should cure her blindness, he should receive from her a sum of money; but if her infirmity remained, she should give him nothing. This agreement being made, the Physician, time after time, applied his salve to her eyes, and on every visit took something away, stealing all her property little by little. And when he had got all she had, he healed her and demanded the promised payment. The Old Woman, when she recovered her sight and saw none of her goods in her house, would give him nothing. The Physician insisted on his claim, and, as she still refused, summoned her before the Judge. The

Old Woman, standing up in the Court, argued: "This man here speaks the truth in what he says; for I did promise to give him a sum of money if I should recover my sight: but if I continued blind, I was to give him nothing. Now he declares that I am healed. I on the contrary affirm that I am still blind; for when I lost the use of my eyes, I saw in my house various chattels and valuable goods: but now, though he swears I am cured of my blindness, I am not able to see a single thing in it."

The Fighting Cocks and the Eagle

TWO GAME COCKS were fiercely fighting for the mastery of the farmyard. One at last put the other to flight. The vanquished Cock skulked away and hid himself in a quiet corner, while the conqueror, flying up to a high wall, flapped his wings and crowed exultingly with all his might. An Eagle sailing through the air pounced upon him and carried him off in his talons. The vanquished Cock immediately came out of his corner, and ruled henceforth with undisputed mastery.

Pride goes before destruction.

The Charger and the Miller

A CHARGER, feeling the infirmities of age, was sent to work in a mill instead of going out to battle. But when he was compelled to grind instead of serving in the wars, he bewailed his change of fortune and called to mind his former state, saying, "Ah! Miller, I had indeed to go campaigning before, but I was barbed from counter to tail, and a man went along to groom me; and now I cannot understand what ailed me to prefer the mill before the battle." "Forbear," said the Miller to him, "harping on what was of yore, for it is the common lot of mortals to sustain the ups and downs of fortune."

The Fox and the Monkey

A MONKEY once danced in an assembly of the Beasts, and so pleased them all by his performance that they elected him their King. A Fox, envying him the honor, discovered a piece of meat lying in a trap, and leading the Monkey to the place where it was, said that she had found a store, but had not used it—she had kept it for him as treasure trove of his kingdom, and counseled him to lay hold of it. The Monkey approached carelessly and was caught in the trap; and on his accusing the Fox of purposely leading him into the snare, she replied, "O Monkey, and are you, with such a mind as yours, going to be King over the Beasts?"

The Horse and His Rider

A HORSE SOLDIER took the utmost pains with his charger. As long as the war lasted, he looked upon him as his fellow-helper in all emergencies and fed him carefully with hay and corn. But when the war was over, he only allowed him chaff to eat and made him carry heavy loads of wood, subjecting him to much slavish drudgery and ill-treatment. War was again proclaimed, however, and when the trumpet summoned him to his standard, the Soldier put on his charger its military trappings, and mounted, being clad in his heavy coat of mail. The Horse

fell down straightway under the weight, no longer equal to
the burden, and said to his master, "You must now go to the war
on foot, for you have transformed me from a Horse into an Ass;
and how can you expect that I can again turn in a moment from
an Ass to a Horse?"

The Belly and the Members

THE MEMBERS of the Body rebelled against the Belly, and said, "Why should we be perpetually engaged in administering to your wants, while you do nothing but take your rest, and enjoy yourself in luxury and self-indulgence?" The Members carried out their resolve and refused their assistance to the Belly. The whole Body quickly became debilitated, and the hands, feet, mouth, and eyes, when too late, repented of their folly.

The Vine and the Goat

A VINE was luxuriant in the time of vintage with leaves and grapes. A Goat, passing by, nibbled its young tendrils and its leaves. The Vine addressed him and said: "Why do you thus injure me without a cause, and crop my leaves? Is there no young grass left? But I shall not have to wait long for my just revenge; for if you now should crop my leaves, and cut me down to my root, I shall provide the wine to pour over you when you are led as a victim to the sacrifice."

Jupiter and the Monkey

JUPITER ISSUED a proclamation to all the beasts of the forest and promised a royal reward to the one whose offspring should be deemed the handsomest. The Monkey came with the rest and presented, with all a mother's tenderness, a flat-nosed, hairless, ill-featured young Monkey as a candidate for the promised reward. A general laugh saluted her on the presentation of her son. She resolutely said, "I know not whether Jupiter will allot the prize to my son, but this I do know, that he is at least in the eyes of me his mother, the dearest, handsomest, and most beautiful of all."

The Widow and Her Little Maidens

A WIDOW who was fond of cleaning had two little maidens to wait on her. She was in the habit of waking them early in the morning, at cockcrow. The maidens, aggravated by such excessive labor, resolved to kill the cock who roused their mistress so early. When they had done this, they found that they had only prepared for themselves greater troubles, for their mistress, no longer hearing the hour from the cock, woke them up to their work in the middle of the night.

The Shepherd's Boy and the Wolf

A SHEPHERD-BOY, who watched a flock of sheep near a village, brought out the villagers three or four times by crying out, "Wolf! Wolf!" and when his neighbors came to help him, laughed at them for their pains. The Wolf, however, did truly come at last. The Shepherd-boy, now really alarmed, shouted in an agony of terror: "Pray, do come and help me; the Wolf is killing the sheep"; but no one paid any heed to his cries, nor rendered any assistance. The Wolf, having no cause of fear, at his leisure lacerated or destroyed the whole flock.

There is no believing a liar, even when he speaks the truth.

The Cat and the Birds

A CAT, hearing that the Birds in a certain aviary were ailing, dressed himself up as a physician, and, taking his cane and a bag of instruments becoming his profession, went to call on them. He knocked at the door and inquired of the inmates how they all did, saying that if they were ill, he would be happy to prescribe for them and cure them. They replied, "We are all very well, and shall continue so, if you will only be good enough to go away, and leave us as we are."

The Kid and the Wolf

A KID standing on the roof of a house, out of harm's way, saw a Wolf passing by and immediately began to taunt and revile him. The Wolf, looking up, said, "Sirrah! I hear thee: yet it is not thou who mockest me, but the roof on which thou art standing."

Time and place often give the advantage to the weak over the strong.

The Ox and the Frog

AN OX drinking at a pool trod on a brood of young frogs and crushed one of them to death. The Mother coming up, and missing one of her sons, inquired of his brothers what had become of him. "He is dead, dear Mother; for just now a very huge beast with four great feet came to the pool and crushed him to death with his cloven heel." The Frog, puffing herself out, inquired, "if the beast was as big as that in size." "Cease, Mother, to puff yourself out," said her son, "and do not be angry; for you would, I assure you, sooner burst than successfully imitate the hugeness of that monster."

The Shepherd and the Wolf

A SHEPHERD once found the whelp of a Wolf and brought it up, and after a while taught it to steal lambs from the neighboring flocks. The Wolf, having shown himself an apt pupil, said to the Shepherd, "Since you have taught me to steal, you must keep a sharp lookout, or you will lose some of your own flock."

The Father and His Two Daughters

A MAN had two daughters, the one married to a gardener, and the other to a tile-maker. After a time he went to the daughter who had married the gardener, and inquired how she was and how all things went with her. She said, "All things are prospering with me, and I have only one wish, that there may be a heavy fall of rain, in order that the plants may be well watered." Not long after, he went to the daughter who had married the tile-maker, and likewise inquired of her how she fared; she replied, "I want for nothing, and have only one wish, that the dry weather may continue, and the sun shine hot and bright, so that the bricks might be dried." He said to her, "If your sister wishes for rain, and you for dry weather, with which of the two am I to join my wishes?"

The Farmer and His Sons

A FARMER, being on the point of death, wished to be sure that his sons would give the same attention to his farm as he himself had given it. He called them to his bedside and said, "My sons, there is a great treasure hid in one of my vineyards." The sons, after his death, took their spades and mattocks and carefully dug over every portion of their land. They found no treasure, but the vines repaid their labor by an extraordinary and superabundant crop.

The Crab and Its Mother

A CRAB said to her son, "Why do you walk so one-sided, my child? It is far more becoming to go straight forward." The young Crab replied: "Quite true, dear Mother; and if you will show me the straight way, I will promise to walk in it." The Mother tried in vain, and submitted without remonstrance to the reproof of her child.

Example is more powerful than precept.

The Heifer and the Ox

A HEIFER saw an Ox hard at work harnessed to a plow, and tormented him with reflections on his unhappy fate in being compelled to labor. Shortly afterwards, at the harvest festival, the owner released the Ox from his yoke, but bound the Heifer with cords and led him away to the altar to be slain in honor of the occasion. The Ox saw what was being done, and said with a smile to the Heifer: "For this you were allowed to live in idleness, because you were presently to be sacrificed."

The Swallow, the Serpent, and the Court of Justice

A SWALLOW, returning from abroad and especially fond of dwelling with men, built herself a nest in the wall of a Court of Justice and there hatched seven young birds. A Serpent gliding past the nest from its hole in the wall ate up the young unfledged nestlings. The Swallow, finding her nest empty, lamented greatly and exclaimed: "Woe to me a stranger! that in this place where all others' rights are protected, I alone should suffer wrong."

The Thief and His Mother

A BOY stole a lesson-book from one of his schoolfellows and took it home to his Mother. She not only abstained from beating him, but encouraged him. He next time stole a cloak and brought it to her, and she again commended him. The Youth, advanced to adulthood, proceeded to steal things of still greater value. At last he was caught in the very act, and having his hands bound behind him, was led away to the place of public execution. His Mother followed in the crowd and violently beat her breast in sorrow, whereupon the young man said, "I wish to say something to my Mother in her ear." She came close to him, and he quickly seized her ear with his teeth and bit it off. The Mother upbraided him as an unnatural child, whereon he replied, "Ah! if you had beaten me when I first stole and brought to you that lesson-book, I should not have come to this, nor have been thus led to a disgraceful death."

The Old Man and Death

AN OLD MAN was employed in cutting wood in the forest, and, in carrying the faggots to the city for sale one day, became very wearied with his long journey. He sat down by the wayside, and throwing down his load, besought "Death" to come. "Death" immediately appeared in answer to his summons and asked for what reason he had called him. The Old Man hurriedly replied, "That, lifting up the load, you may place it again upon my shoulders."

The Fir-Tree and the Bramble

A FIR-TREE said boastingly to the Bramble, "You are useful for nothing at all; while I am everywhere used for roofs and houses." The Bramble answered: "You poor creature, if you would only call to mind the axes and saws which are about to hew you down, you would have reason to wish that you had grown up a Bramble, not a Fir-Tree."

Better poverty without care, than riches with.

The Mouse, the Frog, and the Hawk

A MOUSE who always lived on the land, by an unlucky chance formed an intimate acquaintance with a Frog, who lived for the most part in the water. The Frog, one day intent on mischief, bound the foot of the Mouse tightly to his own. Thus joined together, the Frog first of all led his friend the Mouse to the meadow where they were accustomed to find their food. After this, he gradually led him towards the pool in which he lived, until reaching the very brink, he suddenly jumped in, dragging the Mouse with him. The Frog enjoyed the water amazingly, and swam croaking about, as if he had done a good deed. The unhappy Mouse was soon suffocated by the water, and his dead body floated about on the surface, tied to the foot of the Frog. A Hawk observed it, and, pouncing upon it with his talons, carried it aloft. The Frog, being still fastened to the leg of the Mouse, was also carried off a prisoner, and was eaten by the Hawk.

Harm hatch, harm catch.

The Man Bitten by a Dog

A MAN who had been bitten by a Dog went about in quest of someone who might heal him. A friend, meeting him and learning what he wanted, said, "If you would be cured, take a piece of bread, and dip it in the blood from your wound, and go and give it to the Dog that bit you." The Man who had been bitten laughed at this advice and said, "Why? If I should do so, it would be as if I should beg every Dog in the town to bite me."

Benefits bestowed upon the evil-disposed increase their means of injuring you.

The Two Pots

A RIVER carried down in its stream two Pots, one made of earthenware and the other of brass. The Earthen Pot said to the Brass Pot, "Pray keep at a distance and do not come near me, for if you touch me ever so slightly, I shall be broken in pieces, and besides, I by no means wish to come near you."

Equals make the best friends.

The Wolf and the Sheep

A WOLF, sorely wounded and bitten by dogs, lay sick and maimed in his lair. Being in want of food, he called to a Sheep who was passing, and asked him to fetch some water from a stream flowing close beside him. "For," he said, "if you will bring me drink, I will find means to provide myself with meat." "Yes," said the Sheep, "if I should bring you the draught, you would doubtless make me provide the meat also."

Hypocritical speeches are easily seen through.

The Æthiop

THE PURCHASER of a black servant was persuaded that the color of his skin arose from dirt contracted through the neglect of his former masters. On bringing him home he resorted to every means of cleaning, and subjected the man to incessant scrubbings. The servant caught a severe cold, but he never changed his color or complexion.

What's bred in the bone will stick to the flesh.

The Fisherman and His Nets

A FISHERMAN, engaged in his calling, made a very successful cast and captured a great haul of fish. He managed by a skillful handling of his net to retain all the large fish and to draw them to the shore; but he could not prevent the smaller fish from falling back through the meshes of the net into the sea.

The Huntsman and the Fisherman

A HUNTSMAN, returning with his dogs from the field, fell in by chance with a Fisherman who was bringing home a basket well laden with fish. The Huntsman wished to have the fish, and their owner experienced an equal longing for the contents of the game-bag. They quickly agreed to exchange the produce of their day's sport. Each was so well pleased with his bargain that they made for some time the same exchange day after day. Finally a neighbor said to them, "If you go on in this way, you will soon destroy by frequent use the pleasure of your exchange, and each will again wish to retain the fruits of his own sport."

Abstain and enjoy.

The Old Woman and the Wine-Jar

AN OLD WOMAN found an empty jar which had lately been full of prime old wine and which still retained the fragrant smell of its former contents. She greedily placed it several times to her nose, and drawing it backwards and forwards said, "O most delicious! How nice must the Wine itself have been, when it leaves behind in the very vessel which contained it so sweet a perfume!"

The memory of a good deed lives.

The Fox and the Crow

A CROW having stolen a bit of meat, perched in a tree and held it in her beak. A Fox, seeing this, longed to possess the meat himself, and by a wily stratagem succeeded. "How handsome is the Crow," he exclaimed, "in the beauty of her shape and in the fairness of her complexion! Oh, if her voice were only equal to her beauty, she would deservedly be considered the Queen of Birds!" This he said deceitfully; but the Crow, anxious to refute the reflection cast upon her voice, set up a loud caw and dropped the flesh. The Fox quickly picked it up, and thus addressed the Crow: "My good Crow, your voice is right enough, but your wit is wanting."

The Two Dogs

A MAN had two dogs: a Hound, trained to assist him in his sports, and a Housedog, taught to watch the house. When he returned home after a good day's sport, he always gave the Housedog a large share of his spoil. The Hound, feeling much aggrieved at this, reproached his companion, saying, "It is very hard to have all this labor, while you, who do not assist in the chase, luxuriate on the fruits of my exertions." The Housedog replied, "Do not blame me, my friend, but find fault with the master, who has not taught me to labor, but to depend for subsistence on the labor of others."

Children are not to be blamed for the faults of their parents.

The Stag in the Ox-Stall

A STAG, roundly chased by the hounds and blinded by fear to the danger he was running into, took shelter in a farmyard and hid himself in a shed among the oxen. An Ox gave him this kindly warning: "O unhappy creature! why should you thus, of your own accord, incur destruction and trust yourself in the house of your enemy?" The Stag replied: "Only allow me, friend, to stay where I am, and I will undertake to find some favorable opportunity of effecting my escape." At the approach of the evening the herdsman came to feed his cattle, but did not see the Stag; and even the farm-bailiff with several laborers passed through the shed and failed to notice him. The Stag, congratulating himself on his safety, began to express his sincere thanks to the Oxen who had kindly helped him in the hour of need. One of them again answered him: "We indeed wish you well, but the danger is not over. There is one other yet to pass through the shed, who has as it were a hundred eyes, and until he has come and

gone, your life is still in peril." At that moment the master himself entered, and having had to complain that his oxen had not been properly fed, he went up to their racks and cried out: "Why is there such a scarcity of fodder? There is not half enough straw for them to lie on. Those lazy fellows have not even swept the cobwebs away." While he thus examined everything in turn, he spied the tips of the antlers of the Stag peeping out of the straw. Then summoning his laborers, he ordered that the Stag should be seized and killed.

The Hawk, the Kite, and the Pigeons

THE PIGEONS, terrified by the appearance of a Kite, called upon the Hawk to defend them. He at once consented. When they had admitted him into the cote, they found that he made more havoc and slew a larger number of them in one day than the Kite could pounce upon in a whole year.

Avoid a remedy that is worse than the disease.

The Widow and the Sheep

A CERTAIN poor widow had one solitary Sheep. At shearing time, wishing to take his fleece and to avoid expense, she sheared him herself, but used the shears so unskillfully that with the fleece she sheared the flesh. The Sheep, writhing with pain, said, "Why do you hurt me so, Mistress? What weight can my blood add to the wool? If you want my flesh, there is the butcher, who will kill me in an instant; but if you want my fleece and wool, there is the shearer, who will shear and not hurt me."

The least outlay is not always the greatest gain.

The Wild Ass and the Lion

A WILD ASS and a Lion entered into an alliance so that they might capture the beasts of the forest with greater ease. The Lion agreed to assist the Wild Ass with his strength, while the Wild Ass gave the Lion the benefit of his greater speed. When they had taken as many beasts as their necessities required, the Lion undertook to distribute the prey, and for this purpose divided it into three shares. "I will take the first share," he said, "because I am King: and the second share, as a partner with you in the chase: and the third share (believe me) will be a source of great evil to you, unless you willingly resign it to me, and set off as fast as you can."

Might makes right.

The Eagle and the Arrow

AN EAGLE sat on a lofty rock, watching the movements of a Hare whom he sought to make his prey. An archer, who saw the Eagle from a place of concealment, took an accurate aim and wounded him mortally. The Eagle gave one look at the arrow that had entered his heart and saw in that single glance that its feathers had been furnished by himself. "It is a double grief to me," he exclaimed, "that I should perish by an arrow feathered from my own wings."

The Sick Kite

A KITE, sick unto death, said to his mother: "O Mother! do not mourn, but at once invoke the gods that my life may be prolonged." She replied, "Alas! my son, which of the gods do you think will pity you? Is there one whom you have not outraged by filching from their very altars a part of the sacrifice offered up to them?"

We must make friends in prosperity if we would have their help in adversity.

The Lion and the Dolphin

A LION roaming by the seashore saw a Dolphin lift up its head out of the waves, and suggested that they contract an alliance, saying that of all the animals they ought to be the best friends, since the one was the king of beasts on the earth, and the other was the sovereign ruler of all the inhabitants of the ocean. The

Dolphin gladly consented to this request. Not long afterwards the Lion had a combat with a wild bull, and called on the Dolphin to help him. The Dolphin, though quite willing to give him assistance, was unable to do so, as he could not by any means reach the land. The Lion abused him as a traitor. The Dolphin replied, "Nay, my friend, blame not me, but Nature, which, while giving me the sovereignty of the sea, has quite denied me the power of living upon the land."

The Lion and the Boar

ON A SUMMER DAY, when the great heat induced a general thirst among the beasts, a Lion and a Boar came at the same moment to a small well to drink. They fiercely disputed which of them should drink first, and were soon engaged in the agonies of a mortal combat. When they stopped suddenly to catch their breath for a fiercer renewal of the fight, they saw some Vultures waiting in the distance to feast on the one that should fall first. They at once made up their quarrel, saying, "It is better for us to make friends, than to become the food of Crows or Vultures."

The One-Eyed Doe

A DOE blind in one eye was accustomed to graze as near to the edge of the cliff as she possibly could, in the hope of securing her greater safety. She turned her sound eye towards the land that she might get the earliest tidings of the approach of hunter or hound, and her injured eye towards the sea, from whence she entertained no anticipation of danger. Some boatmen sailing by saw her, and taking a successful aim, mortally wounded her. Yielding up her last breath, she gasped forth this lament: "O wretched creature that I am! to take such precaution against the land, and after all to find this seashore, to which I had come for safety, so much more perilous."

The Shepherd and the Sea

A SHEPHERD, keeping watch over his sheep near the shore, saw the Sea very calm and smooth, and longed to make a voyage with a view to commerce. He sold all his flock, invested it in a cargo of dates, and set sail. But a very great tempest came on, and the ship being in danger of sinking, he threw all his merchandise overboard, and barely escaped with his life in the empty ship. Not long afterwards when someone passed by and observed the unruffled calm of the Sea, he interrupted him and said, "It is again in want of dates, and therefore looks quiet."

The Ass, the Cock, and the Lion

AN ASS and a Cock were in a straw-yard together when a Lion, desperate from hunger, approached the spot. He was about to spring upon the Ass, when the Cock (to the sound of whose voice the Lion, it is said, has a singular aversion) crowed loudly, and the Lion fled away as fast as he could. The Ass, observing his trepidation at the mere crowing of a Cock, summoned courage to attack him, and galloped after him for that purpose. He had run no long distance, when the Lion, turning about, seized him and tore him to pieces.

False confidence often leads into danger.

The Mice and the Weasels

THE WEASELS and the Mice waged a perpetual war with each other, in which much blood was shed. The Weasels were always the victors. The Mice thought that the cause of their frequent defeats was that they had no leaders set apart from the general army to command them, and that they were exposed to dangers from lack of discipline. They therefore chose as leaders Mice that were most renowned for their family descent, strength, and counsel, as well as those most noted for their courage in the fight, so that they might be better marshaled in battle array and formed into troops, regiments, and battalions. When all this was done, and the army disciplined, and the herald Mouse had duly proclaimed war by challenging the Weasels, the newly chosen generals bound their heads with straws, that they might be more conspicuous to all their troops. Scarcely had the battle begun, when a great rout overwhelmed the Mice, who scampered off as fast as they could to their holes. The generals, not being able to get in on account of the ornaments on their heads, were all captured and eaten by the Weasels.

The more honor the more danger.

The Mice in Council

THE MICE summoned a council to decide how they might best devise means of warning themselves of the approach of their great enemy the Cat. Among the many plans suggested, the one that found most favor was the proposal to tie a bell to the neck of the Cat, so that the Mice, being warned by the sound of the tinkling, might run away and hide themselves in their holes at his approach. But when the Mice further debated who among them should thus "bell the Cat," there was no one found to do it.

The Wolf and the Housedog

A WOLF, meeting a big well-fed Mastiff with a wooden collar about his neck, asked him who it was that fed him so well and yet compelled him to drag that heavy log about wherever he went. "The master," he replied. Then said the Wolf: "May no friend of mine ever be in such a plight; for the weight of this chain is enough to spoil the appetite."

The Rivers and the Sea

THE RIVERS joined together to complain to the Sea, saying, "Why is it that when we flow into your tides so potable and sweet, you work in us such a change, and make us salty and unfit to drink?" The Sea, perceiving that they intended to throw the blame on him, said, "Pray cease to flow into me, and then you will not be made briny."

The Playful Ass

AN ASS climbed up to the roof of a building, and frisking about there, broke in the tiling. The owner went up after him and quickly drove him down, beating him severely with a thick wooden cudgel. The Ass said, "Why, I saw the Monkey do this very thing yesterday, and you all laughed heartily, as if it afforded you very great amusement."

The Three Tradesmen

A GREAT CITY was besieged, and its inhabitants were called together to consider the best means of protecting it from the
enemy. A Bricklayer earnestly recommended bricks as affording
the best material for an effective resistance. A Carpenter, with
equal enthusiasm, proposed timber as a preferable method of
defense. Upon which a Currier stood up and said, "Sirs, I differ
from you altogether: there is no material for resistance equal to
a covering of hides; and nothing so good as leather."

Every man for himself.

The Master and His Dogs

A CERTAIN MAN, detained by a storm in his country house, first of
all killed his sheep, and then his goats, for the maintenance of
his household. The storm still continuing, he was obliged to
slaughter his yoke oxen for food. On seeing this, his Dogs took
counsel together, and said, "It is time for us to be off, for if the
master spare not his oxen, who work for his gain, how can we
expect him to spare us?"

He is not to be trusted as a friend who ill-treats his own
family.

The Wolf and the Shepherds

A WOLF, passing by, saw some Shepherds in a hut eating a haunch
of mutton for their dinner. Approaching them, he said, "What
a clamor you would raise if I were to do as you are doing!"

The Dolphins, the Whales, and the Sprat

THE DOLPHINS and Whales waged a fierce war with each other. When the battle was at its height, a Sprat lifted its head out of the waves and said that he would reconcile their differences if they would accept him as an umpire. One of the Dolphins replied, "We would far rather be destroyed in our battle with each other than admit any interference from you in our affairs."

The Ass Carrying the Image

AN ASS once carried through the streets of a city a famous wooden Image, to be placed in one of its Temples. As he passed along, the crowd made lowly prostration before the Image. The Ass, thinking that they bowed their heads in token of respect for himself, bristled up with pride, gave himself airs, and refused to move another step. The driver, seeing him thus stop, laid his whip lustily about his shoulders and said, "O you perverse dull-head! it is not yet come to this, that men pay worship to an Ass."

They are not wise who give to themselves the credit due to others.

The Two Travelers and the Axe

TWO MEN were journeying together. One of them picked up an axe that lay upon the path, and said, "I have found an axe." "Nay, my friend," replied the other, "do not say 'I,' but 'We' have found an axe." They had not gone far before they saw the owner of the axe pursuing them, and he who had picked up the axe said, "We are undone." "Nay," replied the other, "keep to your first mode of speech, my friend; what you thought right then, think right now. Say 'I,' not 'We' are undone."

He who shares the danger ought to share the prize.

The Old Lion

A LION, worn out with years and powerless from disease, lay on the ground at the point of death. A Boar rushed upon him, and avenged with a stroke of his tusks a long-remembered injury. Shortly afterwards the Bull with his horns gored him as if he were an enemy. When the Ass saw that the huge beast could be assailed with impunity, he let drive at his forehead with his heels. The expiring Lion said, "I have reluctantly brooked the insults of the brave, but to be compelled to endure such treatment from thee, a disgrace to Nature, is indeed to die a double death."

The Old Hound

A HOUND, who in the days of his youth and strength had never yielded to any beast of the forest, encountered in his old age a boar in the chase. He seized him boldly by the ear, but could not retain his hold because of the decay of his teeth, so that the boar escaped. His master, quickly coming up, was very much disappointed, and fiercely abused the dog. The Hound looked up and said, "It was not my fault, master; my spirit was as good as ever, but I could not help my infirmities. I rather deserve to be praised for what I have been, than to be blamed for what I am."

The Bee and Jupiter

A BEE from Mount Hymettus, the queen of the hive, ascended to Olympus to present Jupiter some honey fresh from her combs. Jupiter, delighted with the offering of honey, promised to give whatever she should ask. She therefore besought him, saying, "Give me, I pray thee, a sting, that if any mortal shall approach to take my honey, I may kill him." Jupiter was much displeased, for he loved the race of man, but could not refuse the request because of his promise. He thus answered the Bee: "You shall have your request, but it will be at the peril of your own life. For if you use your sting, it shall remain in the wound you make, and then you will die from the loss of it."

Evil wishes, like chickens, come home to roost.

The Milk-Woman and Her Pail

A FARMER's daughter was carrying her Pail of milk from the field to the farmhouse, when she fell a-musing. "The money for which this milk will be sold, will buy at least three hundred eggs. The eggs, allowing for all mishaps, will produce two hundred and fifty chickens. The chickens will become ready for the market when poultry will fetch the highest price, so that by the end of the year I shall have money enough from my share to buy a new gown. In this dress I will go to the Christmas parties, where all the young fellows will propose to me, but I will toss my head and refuse them every one." At this moment she tossed her head in unison with her thoughts, when down fell the Milkpail to the ground, and all her imaginary schemes perished in a moment.

The Seaside Travelers

SOME TRAVELERS, journeying along the seashore, climbed to the summit of a tall cliff, and looking over the sea, saw in the distance what they thought was a large ship. They waited in the hope of seeing it enter the harbor, but as the object on which they looked was driven nearer to shore by the wind, they found that it could at the most be a small boat, and not a ship. When however it reached the beach, they discovered that it was only a large faggot of sticks, and one of them said to his companions, "We have waited for no purpose, for after all there is nothing to see but a load of wood."

Our mere anticipations of life outrun its realities.

The Brazier and His Dog

A BRAZIER had a little Dog, which was a great favorite with his master, and his constant companion. While he hammered away at his metals the Dog slept; but when, on the other hand, he went to dinner and began to eat, the Dog woke up and wagged his tail, as if he would ask for a share of his meal. His master one day, pretending to be angry and shaking his stick at him, said, "You wretched little sluggard! what shall I do to you? While I am hammering on the anvil, you sleep on the mat; and when I begin to eat after my toil, you wake up and wag your tail for food. Do you not know that labor is the source of every blessing, and that none but those who work are entitled to eat?"

The Ass and His Shadow

A TRAVELER hired an Ass to convey him to a distant place. The day being intensely hot, and the sun shining in its strength, the Traveler stopped to rest, and sought shelter from the heat under the Shadow of the Ass. As this afforded only protection for one, and as the Traveler and the owner of the Ass both claimed it, a violent dispute arose between them as to which of them had the right to the Shadow. The owner maintained that he had let

the Ass only, and not his Shadow. The Traveler asserted that he
had, with the hire of the Ass, hired his Shadow also. The quarrel proceeded from words to blows, and while the men fought,
the Ass galloped off.

In quarreling about the shadow we often lose the substance.

The Ass and His Masters

AN ASS, belonging to an herb-seller who gave him too little food
and too much work, made a petition to Jupiter to be released
from his present service and provided with another master. Jupiter, after warning him that he would repent his request, caused
him to be sold to a tile-maker. Shortly afterwards, finding that
he had heavier loads to carry and harder work in the brick-field,
he petitioned for another change of master. Jupiter, telling him
that it would be the last time that he could grant his request,
ordained that he be sold to a tanner. The Ass found that he had
fallen into worse hands, and noting his master's occupation, said,
groaning: "It would have been better for me to have been either
starved by the one, or to have been overworked by the other of
my former masters, than to have been bought by my present
owner, who will even after I am dead tan my hide, and make
me useful to him."

The Oak and the Reeds

A VERY LARGE OAK was uprooted by the wind and thrown across
a stream. It fell among some Reeds, which it thus addressed: "I
wonder how you, who are so light and weak, are not entirely

crushed by these strong winds." They replied, "You fight and contend with the wind, and consequently you are destroyed; while we on the contrary bend before the least breath of air, and therefore remain unbroken, and escape."

Stoop to conquer.

The Fisherman and the Little Fish

A FISHERMAN who lived on the produce of his nets, one day caught a single small Fish as the result of his day's labor. The Fish, panting convulsively, thus entreated for his life: "O Sir, what good can I be to you, and how little am I worth? I am not yet come to my full size. Pray spare my life, and put me back into the sea. I shall soon become a large fish fit for the tables of the rich, and then you can catch me again, and make a handsome profit of me." The Fisherman replied, "I should indeed be a very simple fellow if, for the chance of a greater uncertain profit, I were to forego my present certain gain."

The Hunter and the Woodman

A HUNTER, not very bold, was searching for the tracks of a Lion. He asked a man felling oaks in the forest if he had seen any marks of his footsteps or knew where his lair was. "I will," said the man, "at once show you the Lion himself." The Hunter, turning very pale and chattering with his teeth from fear, replied, "No, thank you. I did not ask that; it is his track only I am in search of, not the Lion himself."

The hero is brave in deeds as well as words.

The Wild Boar and the Fox

A WILD BOAR stood under a tree and rubbed his tusks against the trunk. A Fox passing by asked him why he thus sharpened his teeth when there was no danger threatening from either huntsman or hound. He replied, "I do it advisedly; for it would never do to have to sharpen my weapons just at the time I ought to be using them."

The Lion in a Farmyard

A LION entered a farmyard. The Farmer, wishing to catch him, shut the gate. When the Lion found that he could not escape, he flew upon the sheep and killed them, and then attacked the oxen. The Farmer, beginning to be alarmed for his own safety, opened the gate and released the Lion. On his departure the Farmer grievously lamented the destruction of his sheep and oxen, but his wife, who had been a spectator to all that took place, said, "On my word, you are rightly served, for how could you for a moment think of shutting up a Lion along with you in your farmyard when you know that you shake in your shoes if you only hear his roar at a distance?"

Mercury and the Sculptor

MERCURY ONCE DETERMINED to learn in what esteem he was held among mortals. For this purpose he assumed the character of a man and visited in this disguise a Sculptor's studio. Having looked at various statues, he demanded the price of two figures of Jupiter and Juno. When the sum at which they were valued was named, he pointed to a figure of himself, saying to the Sculptor, "You will certainly want much more for this, as it is the statue of the Messenger of the Gods, and author of all your gain." The Sculptor replied, "Well, if you will buy these, I'll fling you that into the bargain."

The Swan and the Goose

A CERTAIN rich man bought in the market a Goose and a Swan. He fed the one for his table and kept the other for the sake of its song. When the time came for killing the Goose, the cook went to get him at night, when it was dark, and he was not able to distinguish one bird from the other. By mistake he caught the Swan instead of the Goose. The Swan, threatened with death, burst forth into song and thus made himself known by his voice, and preserved his life by his melody.

The Swollen Fox

A VERY HUNGRY FOX, seeing some bread and meat left by shepherds in the hollow of an oak, crept into the hole and made a hearty meal. When he finished, he was so full that he was not able to get out, and began to groan and lament his fate. Another Fox passing by heard his cries, and coming up, inquired the cause of his complaining. On learning what had happened, he said to him, "Ah, you will have to remain there, my friend, until you become such as you were when you crept in, and then you will easily get out."

The Fox and the Woodcutter

A FOX, running before the hounds, came across a Woodcutter felling an oak and begged him to show him a safe hiding-place. The Woodcutter advised him to take shelter in his own hut, so the Fox crept in and hid himself in a corner. The huntsman soon came up with his hounds and inquired of the Woodcutter if he had seen the Fox. He declared that he had not seen him, and yet pointed, all the time he was speaking, to the hut where the Fox lay hidden. The huntsman took no notice of the signs, but believing his word, hastened forward in the chase. As soon as they were well away, the Fox departed without taking any notice of the Woodcutter: whereon he called to him and reproached him, saying, "You ungrateful fellow, you owe your life to me, and yet you leave me without a word of thanks." The Fox replied, "Indeed, I should have thanked you fervently if your deeds had been as good as your words, and if your hands had not been traitors to your speech."

The Birdcatcher, the Partridge, and the Cock

A BIRDCATCHER was about to sit down to a dinner of herbs when a friend unexpectedly came in. The bird-trap was quite empty, as he had caught nothing, and he had to kill a pied Partridge, which he had tamed for a decoy. The bird entreated earnestly for his life: "What would you do without me when next you spread your nets? Who would chirp you to sleep, or call for you the covey of answering birds?" The Birdcatcher spared his life, and determined to pick out a fine young Cock just attaining to his comb. But the Cock expostulated in piteous tones from his perch: "If you kill me, who will announce to you the appearance of the dawn? Who will wake you to your daily tasks or tell you when it is time to visit the bird-trap in the morning?" He replied, "What you say is true. You are a capital bird at telling the time of day. But my friend and I must have our dinners."

Necessity knows no law.

The Monkey and the Fishermen

A MONKEY perched upon a lofty tree saw some Fishermen casting their nets into a river, and narrowly watched their proceedings. The Fishermen after a while gave up fishing, and on going home to dinner left their nets upon the bank. The Monkey, who is the most imitative of animals, descended from the treetop and endeavored to do as they had done. Having handled the net, he threw it into the river, but became tangled in the meshes and drowned. With his last breath he said to himself, "I am rightly served; for what business had I who had never handled a net to try and catch fish?"

The Flea and the Wrestler

A FLEA settled upon the bare foot of a Wrestler and bit him, causing the man to call loudly upon Hercules for help. When the Flea a second time hopped upon his foot, he groaned and said, "O Hercules! if you will not help me against a Flea, how can I hope for your assistance against greater antagonists?"

The Two Frogs

TWO FROGS dwelt in the same pool. When the pool dried up under the summer's heat, they left it and set out together for another home. As they went along they chanced to pass a deep well, amply supplied with water, and when they saw it, one of the Frogs said to the other, "Let us descend and make our abode in this well: it will furnish us with shelter and food." The other replied with greater caution, "But suppose the water should fail us. How can we get out again from so great a depth?"

Do nothing without a regard to the consequences.

The Cat and the Mice

A CERTAIN HOUSE was overrun with Mice. A Cat, discovering this, made her way into it and began to catch and eat them one by one. Fearing for their lives, the Mice kept themselves close in their holes. The Cat was no longer able to get at them and perceived that she must tempt them forth by some device. For this purpose she jumped upon a peg, and suspending herself from it, pretended to be dead. One of the Mice, peeping stealthily out, saw her and said, "Ah, my good madam, even though you should turn into a meal-bag, we will not come near you."

The Lion, the Bear, and the Fox

A LION and a Bear seized a Kid at the same moment, and fought fiercely for its possession. When they had fearfully lacerated each other and were faint from the long combat, they lay down exhausted with fatigue. A Fox, who had gone round them at a distance several times, saw them both stretched on the ground with the Kid lying untouched in the middle. He ran in between them, and seizing the Kid scampered off as fast as he could. The Lion and the Bear saw him, but not being able to get up, said, "Woe be to us, that we should have fought and belabored ourselves only to serve the turn of a Fox!"

It sometimes happens that one man has all the toil, and another all the profit.

The Doe and the Lion

A DOE hard pressed by hunters sought refuge in a cave belonging to a Lion. The Lion concealed himself on seeing her approach, but when she was safe within the cave, sprang upon her and tore her to pieces. "Woe is me," exclaimed the Doe, "who have escaped from man, only to throw myself into the mouth of a wild beast!"

In avoiding one evil, care must be taken not to fall into another.

The Farmer and the Fox

A FARMER, who bore a grudge against a Fox for robbing his poultry yard, caught him at last, and being determined to take an ample revenge, tied some rope well soaked in oil to his tail, and set it on fire. The Fox by a strange fatality rushed to the fields of the Farmer who had captured him. It was the time of the wheat harvest; but the Farmer reaped nothing that year and returned home grieving sorely.

The Seagull and the Kite

A SEAGULL having bolted down too large a fish, burst its deep gullet-bag and lay down on the shore to die. A Kite saw him and exclaimed: "You richly deserve your fate; for a bird of the air has no business to seek its food from the sea."

Every man should be content to mind his own business.

The Philosopher, the Ants, and Mercury

A PHILOSOPHER witnessed from the shore the shipwreck of a vessel, of which the crew and passengers were all drowned. He inveighed against the injustice of Providence, which would for the sake of one criminal perchance sailing in the ship allow so many innocent persons to perish. As he was indulging in these reflections, he found himself surrounded by a whole army of Ants, near whose nest he was standing. One of them climbed up and stung him, and he immediately trampled them all to death with his foot. Mercury presented himself, and striking the Philosopher with his wand, said, "And are you indeed to make yourself a judge of the dealings of Providence, who hast thyself in a similar manner treated these poor Ants?"

The Mouse and the Bull

A BULL was bitten by a Mouse and, angered by the wound, tried to capture him. But the Mouse reached his hole in safety. Though the Bull dug into the walls with his horns, he tired before he could rout out the Mouse, and crouching down, went to sleep outside the hole. The Mouse peeped out, crept furtively up his flank, and again biting him, retreated to his hole. The Bull rising up, and not knowing what to do, was sadly perplexed. At which the Mouse said, "The great do not always prevail. There are times when the small and lowly are the strongest to do mischief."

The Lion and the Hare

A LION came across a Hare, who was fast asleep. He was just in the act of seizing her, when a fine young Hart trotted by, and he left the Hare to follow him. The Hare, scared by the noise, awoke and scudded away. The Lion was unable after a long chase to catch the Hart, and returned to feed upon the Hare. On finding that the Hare also had run off, he said, "I am rightly served, for having let go of the food that I had in my hand for the chance of obtaining more."

The Peasant and the Eagle

A PEASANT found an Eagle captured in a trap, and much admiring the bird, set him free. The Eagle did not prove ungrateful to his deliverer, for seeing the Peasant sitting under a wall which was not safe, he flew toward him and with his talons snatched a bundle from his head. When the Peasant rose in pursuit, the Eagle let the bundle fall again. Taking it up, the man returned to the same place, to find that the wall under which he had been sitting had fallen to pieces; and he marveled at the service rendered him by the Eagle.

The Image of Mercury and the Carpenter

A VERY POOR MAN, a Carpenter by trade, had a wooden image of Mercury, before which he made offerings day by day, and begged the idol to make him rich, but in spite of his entreaties he became poorer and poorer. At last, being very angry, he took his image down from its pedestal, and dashed it against the wall. When its head was knocked off, out came a stream of gold, which the Carpenter quickly picked up and said, "Well, I think thou art altogether contradictory and unreasonable; for when I paid you honor, I reaped no benefits: but now that I maltreat you I am loaded with an abundance of riches."

The Bull and the Goat

A BULL, escaping from a Lion, hid in a cave which some shepherds had recently occupied. As soon as he entered, a He-Goat left in the cave sharply attacked him with his horns. The Bull quietly addressed him: "Butt away as much as you will. I have no fear of you, but of the Lion. Let that monster go away and I will soon let you know what is the respective strength of a Goat and a Bull."

It shows an evil disposition to take advantage of a friend in distress.

The Dancing Monkeys

A PRINCE had some Monkeys trained to dance. Being naturally great mimics of men's actions, they showed themselves most apt pupils; and when arrayed in their rich clothes and masks, they danced as well as any of the courtiers. The spectacle was often repeated with great applause, till on one occasion a courtier, bent on mischief, took from his pocket a handful of nuts and threw them upon the stage. The Monkeys at the sight of the nuts forgot their dancing and became (as indeed they were) Monkeys instead of actors. Pulling off their masks and tearing

their robes, they fought with one another for the nuts. The dancing spectacle thus came to an end amidst the laughter and
ridicule of the audience.

The Fox and the Leopard

THE FOX and the Leopard disputed which was the more beautiful of the two. The Leopard exhibited one by one the various
spots which decorated his skin. But the Fox, interrupting him,
said, "And how much more beautiful than you am I, who am
decorated, not in body, but in mind."

The Monkeys and Their Mother

THE MONKEY, it is said, has two young ones at each birth. The Mother fondles one and nurtures it with the greatest affection and care, but hates and neglects the other. It happened once that the young one which was caressed and loved was smothered by the too great affection of the Mother, while the despised one was nurtured and reared in spite of the neglect to which it was exposed.

The best intentions will not always ensure success.

The Oaks and Jupiter

THE OAKS presented a complaint to Jupiter, saying, "We bear for no purpose the burden of life, as of all the trees that grow we are the most continually in peril of the axe." Jupiter made answer: "You have only to thank yourselves for the misfortunes to which you are exposed: for if you did not make such excellent pillars and posts, and prove yourselves so serviceable to the carpenters and the farmers, the axe would not so frequently be laid to your roots."

The Hare and the Hound

A HOUND started a Hare from his lair, but after a long run, gave up the chase. A goat-herd seeing him stop, mocked him, saying, "The little one is the best runner of the two." The Hound replied, "You do not see the difference between us: I was only running for a dinner, but he for his life."

The Traveler and Fortune

A TRAVELER wearied from a long journey lay down, overcome with fatigue, on the very brink of a deep well. Just as he was about to fall into the water, Dame Fortune, it is said, appeared to him and waking him from his slumber thus addressed him: "Good Sir, pray wake up: for if you fall into the well, the blame will be thrown on me, and I shall get an ill name among mortals; for I find that men are sure to impute their calamities to me, however much by their own folly they have really brought them on themselves."

Everyone is more or less master of his own fate.

The Bald Knight

A BALD KNIGHT, who wore a wig, went out to hunt. A sudden puff of wind blew off his hat and wig, at which a loud laugh rang forth from his companions. He pulled up his horse, and with great glee joined in the joke by saying, "What a marvel it is that hairs which are not mine should fly from me, when they have forsaken even the man on whose head they grew.

The Shepherd and the Dog

A SHEPHERD penning his sheep in the fold for the night was about to shut up a wolf with them, when his Dog perceiving the wolf said, "Master, how can you expect the sheep to be safe if you admit a wolf into the fold?"

The Lamp

A LAMP, soaked with too much oil and flaring brightly, boasted that it gave more light than the sun. Then a sudden puff of wind arose, and the Lamp was immediately extinguished. Its owner lit it again, and said: "Boast no more, but henceforth be content to give thy light in silence. Know that not even the stars need to be relit."

The Lion, the Fox, and the Ass

THE LION, the Fox and the Ass entered into an agreement to assist each other in the chase. Having secured a large booty, the Lion on their return from the forest asked the Ass to allot his due portion to each of the three partners in the treaty. The Ass carefully divided the spoil into three equal shares and modestly requested the two others to make the first choice. The Lion, bursting out into a great rage, devoured the Ass. Then he requested the Fox to do him the favor to make a division. The Fox accumulated all that they had killed into one large heap and left to himself the smallest possible morsel. The Lion said, "Who has taught you, my very excellent fellow, the art of division? You are perfect to a fraction." He replied, "I learned it from the Ass, by witnessing his fate."

Happy is the man who learns from the misfortunes of others.

The Bull, the Lioness, and the Wild-Boar Hunter

A BULL finding a lion's cub asleep gored him to death with his horns. The Lioness came up, and bitterly lamented the death of her whelp. A wild-boar Hunter, seeing her distress, stood at a distance and said to her, "Think how many men there are who have reason to lament the loss of their children, whose deaths have been caused by you."

The Oak and the Woodcutters

THE WOODCUTTERS cut down a Mountain Oak and split it in pieces, making wedges of its own branches for dividing the trunk. The Oak said with a sigh, "I do not care about the blows of the axe aimed at my roots, but I do grieve at being torn in pieces by these wedges made from my own branches."

Misfortunes springing from ourselves are the hardest to bear.

The Hen and the Golden Eggs

A COTTAGER and his wife had a Hen that laid a golden egg every day. They supposed that the Hen must contain a great lump of gold in its inside, and in order to get the gold they killed it. Having done so, they found to their surprise that the Hen differed in no respect from their other hens. The foolish pair, thus hoping to become rich all at once, deprived themselves of the gain of which they were assured day by day.

The Ass and the Frogs

AN ASS, carrying a load of wood, passed through a pond. As he was crossing through the water he lost his footing, stumbled and fell, and not being able to rise on account of his load, groaned heavily. Some Frogs frequenting the pool heard his lamentation, and said, "What would you do if you had to live here always as we do, when you make such a fuss about a mere fall into the water?"

Men often bear little grievances with less courage than they do large misfortunes.

The Crow and the Raven

A CROW was jealous of the Raven, because he was considered a bird of good omen and always attracted the attention of men, who noted by his flight the good or evil course of future events. Seeing some travelers approaching, the Crow flew up into a tree, and perching herself on one of the branches, cawed as loudly as she could. The travelers turned towards the sound and wondered what it foreboded, when one of them said to his companion, "Let us proceed on our journey, my friend, for it is only the caw of a crow, and her cry, you know, is no omen."

Those who assume a character which does not belong to them, only make themselves ridiculous.

The Trees and the Axe

A MAN came into a forest and asked the Trees to provide him a handle for his axe. The Trees consented to his request and gave him a young ash-tree. No sooner had the man fitted a new handle to his axe from it, than he began to use it and quickly felled with his strokes the noblest giants of the forest. An old oak, lamenting when too late the destruction of his companions, said to a neighboring cedar, "The first step has lost us all. If we had not given up the rights of the ash, we might yet have retained our own privileges and have stood for ages."

The Crab and the Fox

A CRAB, forsaking the seashore, chose a neighboring green meadow as its feeding ground. A Fox came across him, and being very hungry ate him up. Just as he was on the point of being eaten, the Crab said, "I well deserve my fate, for what business had I on the land, when by my nature and habits I am only adapted for the sea?"

Contentment with our lot is an element of happiness.

The Woman and Her Hen

A WOMAN possessed a Hen that gave her an egg every day. She often pondered how she might obtain two eggs daily instead of one, and at last, to gain her purpose, determined to give the Hen a double allowance of barley. From that day the Hen became fat and sleek, and never once laid another egg.

The Ass and the Old Shepherd

A SHEPHERD, watching his Ass feeding in a meadow, was alarmed all of a sudden by the cries of the enemy. He appealed to the Ass to fly with him, lest they should both be captured, but the animal lazily replied, "Why should I, pray? Do you think it likely the conqueror will place on me two sets of panniers?" "No," rejoined the Shepherd. "Then," said the Ass, "as long as I carry the panniers, what matters it to me whom I serve?"

In a change of government the poor change nothing beyond the name of their master.

The Kites and the Swans

THE KITES of olden times, as well as the Swans, had the privilege of song. But having heard the neigh of the horse, they were so enchanted with the sound, that they tried to imitate it; and, in trying to neigh, they forgot how to sing.

The desire for imaginary benefits often involves the loss of present blessings.

The Wolves and the Sheepdogs

THE WOLVES thus addressed the Sheepdogs: "Why should you, who are like us in so many things, not be entirely of one mind with us, and live with us as brothers should? We differ from you in one point only. We live in freedom, but you bow down to and slave for men, who in return for your services flog you with whips and put collars on your necks. They make you also guard their sheep, and while they eat the mutton throw only the bones to you. If you will be persuaded by us, you will give us the sheep, and we will enjoy them in common, till we all are surfeited." The Dogs listened favorably to these proposals, and, entering the den of the Wolves, they were set upon and torn to pieces.

The Hares and the Foxes

THE HARES waged war with the Eagles, and called upon the Foxes to help them. They replied, "We would willingly have helped you, if we had not known who you were, and with whom you were fighting."

Count the cost before you commit yourselves.

The Bowman and Lion

A VERY SKILLFUL BOWMAN went to the mountains in search of game, but all the beasts of the forest fled at his approach. The Lion alone challenged him to combat. The Bowman immediately shot out an arrow and said to the Lion: "I send thee my messenger, that from him thou mayest learn what I myself shall be when I assail thee." The wounded Lion rushed away in great fear, and when a Fox who had seen it all happen told him to be of good courage and not to back off at the first attack, he replied: "You counsel me in vain; for if he sends so fearful a messenger, how shall I abide the attack of the man himself?"

Be on guard against men who can strike from a distance.

The Camel

WHEN MAN first saw the Camel, he was so frightened at his vast size that he ran away. After a time, perceiving the meekness and gentleness of the beast's temper, he summoned courage enough to approach him. Soon afterwards, observing that he was an animal altogether deficient in spirit, he assumed such boldness as to put a bridle in his mouth, and to let a child drive him.

Use serves to overcome dread.

The Wasp and the Snake

A WASP seated himself upon the head of a Snake and, striking him unceasingly with his stings, wounded him to death. The Snake, being in great torment and not knowing how to rid himself of his enemy, saw a wagon heavily laden with wood, and went and purposely placed his head under the wheels, saying, "At least my enemy and I shall perish together."

The Dog and the Hare

A HOUND having started a Hare on the hillside pursued her for some distance, at one time biting her with his teeth as if he would take her life, and at another fawning upon her, as if in play with another dog. The Hare said to him, "I wish you would act sincerely by me, and show yourself in your true colors. If you are a friend, why do you bite me so hard? If an enemy, why do you fawn on me?"

No one can be a friend if you know not whether to trust or distrust him.

The Bull and the Calf

A BULL was striving with all his might to squeeze himself through a narrow passage which led to his stall. A young Calf came up, and offered to go before and show him the way by which he could manage to pass. "Save yourself the trouble," said the Bull; "I knew that way long before you were born."

The Stag, the Wolf, and the Sheep

A STAG asked a Sheep to lend him a measure of wheat, and said that the Wolf would be his surety. The Sheep, fearing some fraud was intended, excused herself, saying, "The Wolf is accustomed to seize what he wants and to run off; and you, too, can quickly outstrip me in your rapid flight. How then shall I be able to find you, when the day of payment comes?"

Two blacks do not make one white.

The Peacock and the Crane

A PEACOCK spreading its gorgeous tail mocked a Crane that passed by, ridiculing the ashen hue of its plumage and saying, "I am robed, like a king, in gold and purple and all the colors of the rainbow; while you have not a bit of color on your wings."

"True," replied the Crane; "but I soar to the heights of heaven and lift up my voice to the stars, while you walk below, like a cock, among the birds of the dunghill."

Fine feathers don't make fine birds.

The Fox and the Hedgehog

A FOX swimming across a rapid river was carried by the force of the current into a very deep ravine, where he lay for a long time very much bruised, sick, and unable to move. A swarm of hungry blood-sucking flies settled upon him. A Hedgehog, passing by, saw his anguish and inquired if he should drive away the flies that were tormenting him. "By no means," replied the Fox; "pray do not molest them." "How is this?" said the Hedgehog; "do you not want to be rid of them?" "No," returned the Fox, "for these flies which you see are full of blood, and sting me but little, and if you rid me of these which are already satiated, others more hungry will come in their place, and will drink up all the blood I have left."

The Eagle, the Cat, and the Wild Sow

AN EAGLE made her nest at the top of a lofty oak; a Cat, having found a convenient hole, moved into the middle of the trunk; and a Wild Sow, with her young, took shelter in a hollow at its foot. The Cat cunningly resolved to destroy this chance-made colony. To carry out her design, she climbed to the nest of the Eagle, and said, "Destruction is preparing for you, and for me too, unfortunately. The Wild Sow, whom you see daily digging

up the earth, wishes to uproot the oak, so she may on its fall seize our families as food for her young." Having thus frightened the Eagle out of her senses, she crept down to the cave of the Sow, and said, "Your children are in great danger; for as soon as you go out with your litter to find food, the Eagle is prepared to pounce upon one of your little pigs." Having instilled these fears into the Sow, she went and pretended to hide herself in the hollow of the tree. When night came she went forth with silent foot and obtained food for herself and her kittens, but feigning to be afraid, she kept a lookout all through the day. Meanwhile, the Eagle, full of fear of the Sow, sat still on the branches, and the Sow, terrified by the Eagle, did not dare to go out from her cave. And thus they both, along with their families, perished from hunger, and afforded ample provision for the Cat and her kittens.

The Thief and the Innkeeper

A THIEF hired a room in a tavern and stayed a while in the hope of stealing something which should enable him to pay his reckoning. When he had waited some days in vain, he saw the Innkeeper dressed in a new and handsome coat and sitting before his door. The Thief sat down beside him and talked with him. As the conversation began to flag, the Thief yawned terribly and at the same time howled like a wolf. The Innkeeper said, "Why do you howl so fearfully?" "I will tell you," said the Thief, "but first let me ask you to hold my clothes, or I shall tear them to pieces. I know not, sir, when I got this habit of yawning, nor whether these attacks of howling were inflicted on me as a judgment for my crimes, or for any other cause; but this I do know, that when I yawn for the third time, I actually turn into a wolf and attack men." With this speech he commenced a second fit of yawning and again howled like a wolf, as he had at first. The Innkeeper, hearing his tale and believing what he said, became greatly alarmed and, rising from his seat, attempted to run away. The Thief laid hold of his coat and entreated him to stop, saying, "Pray wait, sir, and hold my clothes, or I shall tear them to pieces in my fury, when I turn into a wolf." At the same moment he yawned the third time and set up a terrible howl. The Innkeeper, frightened lest he should be attacked, left his new coat in the Thief's hand and ran as fast as he could into the inn for safety. The Thief made off with the coat and did not return again to the inn.

Every tale is not to be believed.

The Mule

A MULE, frolicsome from lack of work and from too much corn, galloped about in a very extravagant manner, and said to himself: "My father surely was a high-mettled racer, and I am his own child in speed and spirit." On the next day, being driven a long journey, and feeling very wearied, he exclaimed in a disconsolate tone: "I must have made a mistake; my father, after all, could have been only an ass."

The Hart and the Vine

A HART, hard pressed in the chase, hid himself beneath the large leaves of a Vine. The huntsmen, in their haste, overshot the place of his concealment. Supposing all danger to have passed, the Hart began to nibble the tendrils of the Vine. One of the huntsmen, attracted by the rustling of the leaves, looked back, and seeing the Hart, shot an arrow from his bow and struck it. The Hart, at the point of death, groaned: "I am rightly served, for I should not have maltreated the Vine that saved me."

The Serpent and the Eagle

A SERPENT and an Eagle were struggling with each other in deadly conflict. The Serpent had the advantage, and was about to strangle the bird. A countryman saw them, and running up, loosed the coil of the Serpent and let the Eagle go free. The Serpent, irritated at the escape of his prey, injected his poison into the drinking horn of the countryman. The rustic, ignorant of his danger, was about to drink, when the Eagle struck his hand with his wing, and, seizing the drinking horn in his talons, carried it aloft.

The Crow and the Pitcher

A CROW perishing with thirst saw a pitcher, and hoping to find water, flew to it with delight. When he reached it, he discovered to his grief that it contained so little water that he could not possibly get at it. He tried everything he could think of to reach the water, but all his efforts were in vain. At last he collected as many stones as he could carry and dropped them one by one with his beak into the pitcher, until he brought the water within his reach and thus saved his life.

Necessity is the mother of invention.

The Two Frogs

TWO FROGS were neighbors. One inhabited a deep pond, far removed from public view; the other lived in a gully containing little water, and traversed by a country road. The Frog that lived in the pond warned his friend to change his residence and entreated him to come and live with him, saying that he would enjoy greater safety from danger and more abundant food. The other refused, saying that he felt it so very hard to leave a place to which he had become accustomed. A few days afterwards a heavy wagon passed through the gully and crushed him to death under its wheels.

A willful man will have his way to his own hurt.

The Wolf and the Fox

AT ONE TIME a very large and strong Wolf was born among the wolves, who exceeded all his fellow-wolves in strength, size, and swiftness, so that they unanimously decided to call him "Lion." The Wolf, with a lack of sense proportioned to his enormous size, thought that they gave him this name in earnest, and, leaving his own race, consorted exclusively with the lions. An old sly Fox, seeing this, said, "May I never make myself so ridiculous as you do in your pride and self-conceit; for even though you have the size of a lion among wolves, in a herd of lions you are definitely a wolf."

The Walnut-Tree

A WALNUT-TREE standing by the roadside bore an abundant crop of fruit. For the sake of the nuts, the passers-by broke its branches with stones and sticks. The Walnut-Tree piteously exclaimed, "O wretched me! that those whom I cheer with my fruit should repay me with these painful requitals!"

The Gnat and the Lion

A GNAT came and said to a Lion, "I do not in the least fear you, nor are you stronger than I am. For in what does your strength consist? You can scratch with your claws and bite with your teeth—so can a woman in her quarrels. I repeat that I am altogether more powerful than you; and if you doubt it, let us fight and see who will conquer." The Gnat, having sounded his horn, fastened himself upon the Lion and stung him on the nostrils and the parts of the face devoid of hair. While trying to crush him, the Lion tore himself with his claws, until he punished himself severely. The Gnat thus prevailed over the Lion, and, buzzing about in a song of triumph, flew away. But shortly afterwards he became entangled in the meshes of a cobweb and was eaten by a spider. He greatly lamented his fate, saying, "Woe is me! that I, who can wage war successfully with the hugest beasts, should perish myself from this spider, the most inconsiderable of insects!"

The Monkey and the Dolphin

A SAILOR, bound on a long voyage, took with him a Monkey to amuse him while on shipboard. As he sailed off the coast of Greece, a violent tempest arose in which the ship was wrecked, and he, his Monkey, and all the crew were obliged to swim for their lives. A Dolphin saw the Monkey contending with the waves, and supposing him to be a man (whom he is always said to befriend), came and placed himself under him, to convey him on his back in safety to the shore. When the Dolphin arrived with his burden in sight of land not far from Athens, he asked the Monkey if he were an Athenian. The latter replied that he was, and that he was descended from one of the most noble families in that city. The Dolphin then inquired if he knew the Piraeus (the famous harbor of Athens). Supposing that a man was meant, the Monkey answered that he knew him very well and that he was an intimate friend. The Dolphin, indignant at these falsehoods, dipped the Monkey under the water and drowned him.

The Jackdaw and the Doves

A JACKDAW, seeing some Doves in a cote abundantly provided with food, painted himself white and joined them in order to share their plentiful maintenance. The Doves, as long as he was silent, supposed him to be one of themselves and admitted him to their cote. But when one day he forgot himself and began to chatter, they discovered his true character and drove him forth, pecking him with their beaks. Failing to obtain food among the Doves, he returned to the Jackdaws. They too, not recognizing him on account of his color, expelled him from living with them. So desiring two ends, he obtained neither.

The Horse and the Stag

AT ONE TIME the Horse had the plain entirely to himself. Then a Stag intruded into his domain and shared his pasture. The Horse, desiring to revenge himself on the stranger, asked a man if he were willing to help him in punishing the Stag. The man replied that if the Horse would receive a bit in his mouth and agree to carry him, he would contrive effective weapons against the Stag. The Horse consented and allowed the man to mount him. From that hour he found that instead of obtaining revenge on the Stag, he had enslaved himself to the service of man.

The Kid and the Wolf

A KID, returning without protection from the pasture, was pursued by a Wolf. Seeing he could not escape, he turned round, and said: "I know, friend Wolf, that I must be your prey, but before I die I would ask of you one favor—that you will play me a tune to which I may dance." The Wolf complied, and while he was piping and the Kid was dancing, some hounds hearing the sound ran up and began chasing the Wolf. Turning to the Kid, he said, "It is just what I deserve; for I, who am only a butcher, should not have turned piper to please you."

The Prophet

A WIZARD, sitting in the marketplace, was telling the fortunes of the passers-by when a person ran up in great haste, and announced to him that the doors of his house had been broken open, and that all his goods were being stolen. He sighed heavily and hastened away as fast as he could run. A neighbor saw him running and said, "Oh! you fellow there! you say you can foretell the fortunes of others; how is it you did not foresee your own?"

The Fox and the Monkey

A FOX and a Monkey were traveling together on the same road. As they journeyed, they passed through a cemetery full of monuments. "All these monuments which you see," said the Monkey, "are erected in honor of my ancestors, who were in their day freedmen and citizens of great renown." The Fox replied, "You have chosen a most appropriate subject for your falsehoods, as I am sure none of your ancestors will be able to contradict you."

A false tale often betrays itself.

The Thief and the Housedog

A THIEF came in the night to break into a house. He brought with him several slices of meat in order to pacify the Housedog, so that he would not alarm his master by barking. As the Thief threw him the pieces of meat, the Dog said, "If you think to stop my mouth, you will be greatly mistaken. This sudden kindness at your hands will only make me more watchful, lest under these unexpected favors to myself, you have some private ends to accomplish for your own benefit, and for my master's injury."

The Man, the Horse, the Ox, and the Dog

A HORSE, Ox, and Dog, driven to great straits by the cold, sought shelter and protection from Man. He received them kindly, lighted a fire, and warmed them. He let the Horse make free with his oats, gave the Ox an abundance of hay, and fed the

Dog with meat from his own table. Grateful for these favors, the animals determined to repay him to the best of their ability. For this purpose, they divided the term of his life between them, and each endowed one portion of it with the qualities which chiefly characterized himself. The Horse chose his earliest years and gave them his own attributes: hence every man is in his youth impetuous, headstrong, and obstinate in maintaining his own opinion. The Ox took under his patronage the next term of life, and therefore man in his middle age is fond of work, devoted to labor, and resolute to amass wealth and to husband his resources. The end of life was reserved for the Dog, wherefore the old man is often snappish, irritable, hard to please, and selfish, tolerant only of his own household, but averse to strangers and to all who do not administer to his comfort or to his necessities.

The Apes and the Two Travelers

TWO MEN, one who always spoke the truth and the other who told nothing but lies, were traveling together and by chance came to the land of Apes. One of the Apes, who had raised himself to be king, commanded them to be seized and brought before him, that he might know what was said of him among men. He ordered at the same time that all the Apes be arranged in a long row on his right hand and on his left, and that a throne be placed for him, as was the custom among men. After these preparations he signified that the two men should be brought before him, and greeted them with this salutation: "What sort of a king do I seem to you to be, O strangers?" The lying Traveler replied, "You seem to me a most mighty king." "And what is your estimate of those you see around me?" "These," he made answer, "are worthy companions of yourself, fit at least to be ambassadors and leaders of armies." The Ape and all his court, gratified with the lie, commanded that a handsome present be given to the flatterer. On this the truthful Traveler thought to himself, "If so great a reward be given for a lie, with what gift may not I be rewarded, if, according to my custom, I tell the truth?" The Ape quickly turned to him. "And pray how do I and these my friends around me seem to you?" "Thou art," he said, "a most excellent Ape, and all these thy companions after thy example are excellent Apes too." The King of the Apes, enraged at hearing these truths, gave him over to the teeth and claws of his companions.

The Wolf and the Shepherd

A WOLF followed a flock of sheep for a long time and did not attempt to injure one of them. The Shepherd at first stood on his guard against him, as against an enemy, and kept a strict watch over his movements. But when the Wolf, day after day, kept in the company of the sheep and did not make the slightest effort to seize them, the Shepherd began to look upon him as a guardian of his flock rather than as a plotter of evil against it; and when occasion called him one day into the city, he left the sheep entirely in his charge. The Wolf, now that he had the opportunity, fell upon the sheep, and destroyed the greater part of the flock. When the Shepherd returned to find his flock destroyed, he exclaimed: "I have been rightly served; why did I trust my sheep to a Wolf?"

The Hares and the Lions

THE HARES harangued the assembly, and argued that all should be equal. The Lions made this reply: "Your words, O Hares! are good; but they lack both claws and teeth such as we have."

The Lark and Her Young Ones

A LARK had made her nest in the early spring on the young green wheat. The brood had almost grown to their full strength and attained the use of their wings and the full plumage of their feathers, when the owner of the field, looking over his ripe crop, said, "The time has come when I must ask all my neighbors to help me with my harvest." One of the young Larks heard his speech and related it to his mother, inquiring of her to what place they should move for safety. "There is no occasion to move yet, my son," she replied; "the man who only sends to his friends to help him with his harvest is not really in earnest." The owner of the field came again a few days later and saw the wheat shedding the grain from excess of ripeness. He said, "I will come myself tomorrow with my laborers, and with as many reapers as I can hire, and will get in the harvest." The Lark, on hearing these words said to her brood, "It is time now to be off, my little ones, for the man is in earnest this time; he no longer trusts his friends, but will reap the field himself."

Self-help is the best help.

The Fox and the Lion

WHEN A FOX who had never yet seen a Lion, fell in with him by chance for the first time in the forest, he was so frightened that he nearly died with fear. On meeting him for the second time, he was still much alarmed, but not to the same extent as at first. On seeing him the third time, he so increased in boldness that he went up to him and commenced a familiar conversation with him.

Acquaintance softens prejudices.

The Weasel and the Mice

A WEASEL, inactive from age and infirmities, was not able to catch mice as he once did. He therefore rolled himself in flour and lay down in a dark corner. A Mouse, supposing him to be food, leaped upon him, and was instantly caught and squeezed to death. Another perished in a similar manner, and then a third, and still others after them. A very old Mouse, who had escaped many a trap and snare, observed from a safe distance the trick of his crafty foe and said, "Ah! you that lie there, may you prosper just in the same proportion as you are what you pretend to be!"

The Boy Bathing

A BOY bathing in a river was in danger of being drowned. He called out to a passing traveler for help, but instead of holding out a helping hand, the man stood by unconcernedly, and scolded the boy for his imprudence. "Oh, sir!" cried the youth, "pray help me now and scold me afterwards."

Counsel without help is useless.

The Ass and the Wolf

AN ASS feeding in a meadow saw a Wolf approaching to seize him, and immediately pretended to be lame. The Wolf, coming up, inquired the cause of his lameness. The Ass replied that passing through a hedge he had trod with his foot upon a sharp thorn. He requested that the Wolf pull it out, lest when he ate him it should injure his throat. The Wolf consented and lifted up the foot, and was giving his whole mind to the discovery of the thorn, when the Ass, with his heels, kicked his teeth into his mouth and galloped away. The Wolf, being thus fearfully mauled, said, "I am rightly served, for why did I attempt the art of healing, when my father only taught me the trade of a butcher?"

The Seller of Images

A CERTAIN MAN made a wooden image of Mercury and offered it for sale. When no one appeared willing to buy it, in order to attract purchasers, he cried out that he had the statue to sell of a benefactor who bestowed wealth and helped to heap up riches. One of the bystanders said to him, "My good fellow, why do you sell him, being such a one as you describe, when you may yourself enjoy the good things he has to give?" "Why," he replied, "I am in need of immediate help, and he is wont to give his good gifts very slowly."

The Fox and the Grapes

A FAMISHED FOX saw some clusters of ripe black grapes hanging from a trellised vine. She resorted to all her tricks to get at them, but wearied herself in vain, for she could not reach them. At last she turned away, hiding her disappointment and saying: "The Grapes are sour, and not ripe as I thought."

The Man and His Wife

A MAN had a Wife who made herself hated by all the members of his household. Wishing to find out if she had the same effect on the persons in her father's house, he made some excuse to send her home on a visit to her father. After a short time she returned, and when he inquired how she had got on and how the servants had treated her, she replied, "The herdsmen and shepherds cast on me looks of aversion." He said, "O Wife, if you were disliked by those who go out early in the morning with their flocks and return late in the evening, what must have been felt towards you by those with whom you passed the whole day!"

Straws show how the wind blows.

The Peacock and Juno

THE PEACOCK made complaint to Juno that, while the nightingale pleased every ear with his song, he himself no sooner opened his mouth than he became a laughingstock to all who heard him. The Goddess, to console him, said, "But you far excel in beauty and in size. The splendor of the emerald shines in your neck, and you unfold a tail gorgeous with painted plumage." "But for what purpose have I," said the bird, "this dumb beauty so long as I am surpassed in song?" "The lot of each," replied Juno, "has been assigned by the will of the Fates—to thee, beauty; to the eagle, strength; to the nightingale, song; to the raven, favorable, and to the crow, unfavorable, auguries. These are all contented with the endowments allotted to them."

The Hawk and the Nightingale

A NIGHTINGALE, sitting aloft upon an oak and singing according to his wont, was seen by a Hawk who, being in need of food, swooped down and seized him. The Nightingale, about to lose his life, earnestly begged the Hawk to let him go, saying that he was not big enough to satisfy the hunger of a Hawk, who, if he wanted food, ought to pursue the larger birds. The Hawk, interrupting him, said: "I should indeed have lost my senses if I should let go food ready in my hand, for the sake of pursuing birds which are not yet even within sight."

The Dog, the Cock, and the Fox

A DOG and a Cock, being great friends, agreed to travel together. At nightfall they took shelter in a thick wood. The Cock, flying up, perched himself on the branches of a tree, while the Dog found a bed beneath in the hollow trunk. When the morning dawned, the Cock, as usual, crowed very loudly several times. A Fox heard the sound, and wishing to make a breakfast on him, came and stood under the branches, saying how earnestly he desired to make the acquaintance of the owner of so magnificent a voice. The Cock, suspecting his civilities, said: "Sir, I wish you would do me the favor of going around to the hollow trunk below me, and waking my porter, so that he may open the door and let you in." When the Fox approached the tree, the Dog sprang out and caught him, and tore him to pieces.

The Wolf and the Goat

A WOLF saw a Goat feeding at the summit of a steep precipice, where he had no chance of reaching her. He called to her and earnestly begged her to come lower down, lest she fall by some mishap; and he added that the meadows lay where he was standing, and that the herbage was most tender. She replied, "No, my friend, it is not for the pasture that you invite me, but for yourself, who are in want of food."

The Lion and the Bull

A LION, greatly desiring to capture a Bull, and yet afraid to attack him on account of his great size, resorted to a trick to ensure his destruction. He approached the Bull and said, "I have slain a fine sheep, my friend; and if you will come home and partake of him with me, I shall be delighted to have your company." The Lion said this in the hope that, as the Bull was in the act of reclining to eat, he might attack him to advantage, and make his meal on him. The Bull, on approaching the Lion's den, saw the huge spits and giant caldrons, and no sign whatever of the sheep, and, without saying a word, quietly took his departure. The Lion inquired why he went off so abruptly without a word of salutation to his host, who had not given him any cause for offense. "I have reasons enough," said the Bull. "I see no indication whatever of your having slaughtered a sheep, while I do see very plainly every preparation for your dining on a bull."

The Goat and the Ass

A MAN once kept a Goat and an Ass. The Goat, envying the Ass on account of his greater abundance of food, said, "How shamefully you are treated: at one time grinding in the mill, and at another carrying heavy burdens"; and he further advised him to pretend to be epileptic and fall into a ditch and so obtain rest. The Ass listened to his words, and falling into a ditch, was very much bruised. His master, sending for a leech, asked his advice. He bade him pour upon the wounds the lungs of a Goat. They at once killed the Goat, and so healed the Ass.

The Town Mouse and the Country Mouse

A COUNTRY MOUSE invited a Town Mouse, an intimate friend, to pay him a visit and partake of his country fare. As they were on the bare plowlands, eating their wheat-stalks and roots pulled up from the hedgerow, the Town Mouse said to his friend, "You live here the life of the ants, while in my house is the horn of plenty. I am surrounded with every luxury, and if you will come with me, as I wish you would, you shall have an ample share of my dainties." The Country Mouse was easily persuaded, and returned to town with his friend. On his arrival, the Town Mouse placed before him bread, barley, beans, dried figs, honey, raisins, and, last of all, brought a dainty piece of cheese from a basket. The Country Mouse, being much delighted at the sight of such good cheer, expressed his satisfaction in warm terms and lamented his own hard fate. Just as they were beginning to eat, someone opened the door, and they both ran off squeaking, as fast as they could, to a hole so narrow that two could only find room in it by squeezing. They had scarcely begun their repast again when someone else entered to take something out of a cupboard, whereupon the two Mice, more frightened than before, ran away and hid themselves. At last the Country Mouse, almost famished, said to his friend: "Although you have prepared for me so dainty a feast, I must leave you to enjoy it by yourself. It is surrounded by too many dangers to please me. I prefer my bare plowlands and roots from the hedgerow, where I can live in safety, and without fear."

The Wolf, the Fox, and the Ape

A WOLF accused a Fox of theft, but the Fox entirely denied the charge. An Ape undertook to adjudge the matter between them. When each had fully stated his case, the Ape pronounced this sentence: "I do not think you, Wolf, ever lost what you claim; and I do believe you, Fox, to have stolen what you so stoutly deny."

The dishonest, if they act honestly, get no credit.

The Fly and the Draught-Mule

A FLY sat on the axle-tree of a chariot, and addressing the Draught-Mule said, "How slow you are! Why do you not go faster? See if I do not prick your neck with my sting." The Draught-Mule replied, "I do not heed your threats; I only care for him who sits above you, and who quickens my pace with his whip, or holds me back with the reins. Away, therefore, with your insolence, for I know well when to go fast, and when to go slow."

The Fishermen

SOME FISHERMEN were out trawling their nets. Perceiving them to be very heavy, they danced about for joy and supposed that they had taken a large catch. When they had dragged the nets to the shore they found but few fish: the nets were full of sand and stones, and the men were beyond measure cast down—not so much at the disappointment which had befallen them, but because they had formed such very different expectations. One of their company, an old man, said, "Let us cease lamenting, my mates, for, as it seems to me, sorrow is always the twin sister of joy; and it was only to be looked for that we, who just now were over-rejoiced, should next have something to make us sad."

The Lion and the Three Bulls

THREE BULLS for a long time pastured together. A Lion lay in ambush in the hope of making them his prey, but was afraid to attack them while they kept together. Having at last by guileful speeches succeeded in separating them, he attacked them without fear as they fed alone, and feasted on them one by one at his own leisure.

Union is strength.

The Fowler and the Viper

A FOWLER, taking his bird-lime and his twigs, went out to catch birds. Seeing a thrush sitting upon a tree, he wished to take it, and fitting his twigs to a proper length, watched intently, having his whole thoughts directed towards the sky. While thus looking upwards, he unknowingly trod upon a Viper asleep just before his feet. The Viper, turning about, stung him, and falling into a swoon, the man said to himself, "Woe is me! that while I purposed to hunt another, I am myself fallen unawares into the snares of death."

The Horse and the Ass

A HORSE, proud of his fine trappings, met an Ass on the highway. The Ass, being heavily laden, moved slowly out of the way. "Hardly," said the Horse, "can I resist kicking you with my heels." The Ass held his peace, and made only a silent appeal to the justice of the gods. Not long afterwards the Horse, having become broken-winded, was sent by his owner to the farm. The Ass, seeing him drawing a dungcart, thus derided him: "Where, O boaster, are now all thy gay trappings, thou who are thyself reduced to the condition you so lately treated with contempt?"

The Fox and the Mask

A FOX entered the house of an actor and, rummaging through all his properties, came upon a Mask, an admirable imitation of a human head. He placed his paws on it and said, "What a beautiful head! Yet it is of no value, as it entirely lacks brains."

The Geese and the Cranes

THE GEESE and the Cranes were feeding in the same meadow, when a birdcatcher came to ensnare them in his nets. The Cranes, being light of wing, fled away at his approach; while the Geese, being slower of flight and heavier in their bodies, were captured.

The Blind Man and the Whelp

A BLIND MAN was accustomed to distinguishing different animals by touching them with his hands. The whelp of a Wolf was brought him, with a request that he would feel it, and say what it was. He felt it, and being in doubt, said: "I do not quite know whether it is the cub of a Fox, or the whelp of a Wolf, but this I know full well. It would not be safe to admit him to the sheepfold."

Evil tendencies are shown in early life.

The Dogs and the Fox

SOME DOGS, finding the skin of a lion, began to tear it in pieces with their teeth. A Fox, seeing them, said, "If this lion were alive, you would soon find out that his claws were stronger than your teeth."

It is easy to kick a man that is down.

The Cobbler Turned Doctor

A COBBLER unable to make a living by his trade and made desperate by poverty, began to practice medicine in a town in which he was not known. He sold a drug, pretending that it was an antidote to all poisons, and obtained a great name for himself by long-winded puffs and advertisements. When the Cobbler happened to fall sick himself of a serious illness, the Governor of the town determined to test his skill. For this purpose he called for a cup, and while filling it with water, pretended to mix poison with the Cobbler's antidote, commanding him to drink it on the promise of a reward. The Cobbler, under the fear of death, confessed that he had no knowledge of medicine, and was only made famous by the stupid clamors of the crowd. The Governor then called a public assembly and addressed the citizens: "Of what folly have you been guilty? You have not hesitated to entrust your heads to a man, whom no one could employ to make even the shoes for their feet."

The Wolf and the Horse

A WOLF coming out of a field of oats met a Horse and thus addressed him: "I would advise you to go into that field. It is full of fine oats, which I have left untouched for you, as you are a friend whom I would love to hear enjoying good eating." The Horse replied, "If oats had been the food of wolves, you would never have indulged your ears at the cost of your belly."

Men of evil reputation, when they perform a good deed, fail to get credit for it.

The Brother and the Sister

A FATHER had one son and one daughter, the former remarkable for his good looks, the latter for her extraordinary ugliness. While they were playing one day as children, they happened by chance to look together into a mirror that was placed on their mother's chair. The boy congratulated himself on his good looks; the girl grew angry, and could not bear the self-praises of her Brother, interpreting all he said (and how could she do otherwise?) into reflection on herself. She ran off to her father, to be avenged on her Brother, and spitefully accused him of having, as a boy, made use of that which belonged only to girls. The father embraced them both, and bestowing his kisses and affection impartially on each, said, "I wish you both would look into the mirror every day: you, my son, that you may not spoil your beauty by evil conduct; and you, my daughter, that you may make up for your lack of beauty by your virtues."

The Wasps, the Partridges, and the Farmer

THE WASPS and the Partridges, overcome with thirst, came to a Farmer and besought him to give them some water to drink. They promised amply to repay him the favor which they asked. The Partridges declared that they would dig around his vines and make them produce finer grapes. The Wasps said that they would keep guard and drive off thieves with their stings. But the Farmer interrupted them, saying: "I have already two oxen, who, without making any promises, do all these things. It is surely better for me to give the water to them than to you."

The Crow and Mercury

A CROW caught in a snare prayed to Apollo to release him, making a vow to offer some frankincense at his shrine. But when rescued from his danger, he forgot his promise. Shortly afterwards, again caught in a snare, he passed by Apollo and made the same promise to offer frankincense to Mercury. Mercury soon appeared and said to him, "O thou most base fellow? how can I believe thee, who hast disowned and wronged thy former patron?"

The North Wind and the Sun

THE NORTH WIND and the Sun disputed as to which was the most powerful, and agreed that he should be declared the victor who could first strip a wayfaring man of his clothes. The North Wind first tried his power and blew with all his might, but the keener his blasts, the closer the Traveler wrapped his cloak around him, until at last, resigning all hope of victory, the Wind called upon the Sun to see what he could do. The Sun suddenly shone out with all his warmth. The Traveler no sooner felt his genial rays than he took off one garment after another, and at last, fairly overcome with heat, undressed and bathed in a stream that lay in his path.

Persuasion is better than Force.

The Two Men Who Were Enemies

TWO MEN, deadly enemies to each other, were sailing in the same vessel. Determined to keep as far apart as possible, the one seated himself in the stern, and the other in the prow of the ship. A violent storm arose, and with the vessel in great danger of sinking, the one in the stern inquired of the pilot which of the two ends of the ship would go down first. On his replying that he supposed it would be the prow, the Man said, "Death would not be grievous to me, if I could only see my Enemy die before me."

The Gamecocks and the Partridge

A MAN had two Gamecocks in his poultry-yard. One day by chance he found a tame Partridge for sale. He purchased it and brought it home to be reared with his Gamecocks. When the Partridge was put into the poultry-yard, they struck at it and followed it about, so that the Partridge became grievously troubled and supposed that he was thus evilly treated because he was a stranger. Not long afterwards he saw the Cocks fighting together and not separating before one had well beaten the other. He then said to himself, "I shall no longer distress myself at being struck at by these Gamecocks, when I see that they cannot even refrain from quarreling with each other."

The Quack Frog

A FROG once upon a time came forth from his home in the marsh and proclaimed to all the beasts that he was a learned physician, skilled in the use of drugs and able to heal all diseases. A Fox asked him, "How can you pretend to prescribe for others, when you are unable to heal your own lame gait and wrinkled skin?"

The Lion, the Wolf, and the Fox

A LION, growing old, lay sick in his cave. All the beasts came to visit their king, except the Fox. The Wolf therefore, thinking that he had a capital opportunity, accused the Fox to the Lion of not paying any respect to him who had the rule over them all and of not coming to visit him. At that very moment the Fox came in and heard these last words of the Wolf. The Lion roaring out in a rage against him, the Fox sought an opportunity to defend himself and said, "And who of all those who have come to you have benefited you so much as I, who have traveled from place to place in every direction, and have sought and learnt from the physicians the means of healing you?" The Lion commanded him immediately to tell him the cure, when he replied, "You must flay a wolf alive and wrap his skin yet warm around you." The Wolf was at once taken and flayed; whereon the Fox, turning to him, said with a smile, "You should have moved your master not to ill, but to good, will."

The Dog's House

IN THE WINTERTIME, a Dog curled up in as small a space as possible on account of the cold, determined to make himself a house. However when the summer returned again, he lay asleep stretched at his full length and appeared to himself to be of a great size. Now he considered that it would be neither an easy nor a necessary work to make himself such a house as would accommodate him.

The Wolf and the Lion

ROAMING BY the mountainside at sundown, a Wolf saw his own shadow become greatly extended and magnified, and he said to himself, "Why should I, being of such an immense size and extending nearly an acre in length, be afraid of the Lion? Ought I not to be acknowledged as King of all the collected beasts?" While he was indulging in these proud thoughts, a Lion fell upon him and killed him. He exclaimed with a too late repentance, "Wretched me! this overestimation of myself is the cause of my destruction."

The Birds, the Beasts, and the Bat

THE BIRDS waged war with the Beasts, and each were by turns the conquerors. A Bat, fearing the uncertain issues of the fight, always fought on the side which he felt was the strongest. When peace was proclaimed, his deceitful conduct was apparent to both combatants. Therefore being condemned by each for his treachery, he was driven forth from the light of day, and henceforth concealed himself in dark hiding-places, flying always alone and at night.

The Spendthrift and the Swallow

A YOUNG MAN, a great spendthrift, had run through all his patrimony and had but one good cloak left. One day he happened to see a Swallow, which had appeared before its season, skimming along a pool and twittering gaily. He supposed that summer had come, and went and sold his cloak. Not many days later, winter set in again with renewed frost and cold. When he found the unfortunate Swallow lifeless on the ground, he said, "Unhappy bird! what have you done? By thus appearing before the springtime you have not only killed yourself, but you have wrought my destruction also."

The Fox and the Lion

A FOX saw a Lion confined in a cage, and standing near him, bitterly reviled him. The Lion said to the Fox, "It is not thou who revilest me; but this mischance which has befallen me."

The Owl and the Birds

AN OWL, in her wisdom, counseled the Birds that when the acorn first began to sprout, to pull it all up out of the ground and not allow it to grow. She said acorns would produce mistletoe, from which an irremediable poison, the bird-lime, would be extracted, and by which they would be captured. The Owl next advised them to pluck up the seed of the flax, which men had sown, as it was a plant which boded no good to them. And, lastly, the Owl, seeing an archer approach, predicted that this man, being on foot, would contrive darts armed with feathers which would fly faster than the wings of the Birds themselves. The Birds gave no credence to these warning words, but considered the Owl to be beside herself and said that she was mad. But afterwards, finding her words were true, they wondered at her knowledge and deemed her to be the wisest of birds. Hence it is that when she appears they look to her as knowing all things, while she no longer gives them advice, but in solitude laments their past folly.

The Trumpeter Taken Prisoner

A TRUMPETER, bravely leading on the soldiers, was captured by the enemy. He cried out to his captors, "Pray spare me, and do not take my life without cause or without inquiry. I have not slain a single man of your troop. I have no arms, and carry nothing but this one brass trumpet." "That is the very reason for which you should be put to death," they said; "for, while you do not fight yourself, your trumpet stirs all the others to battle."

The Ass in the Lion's Skin

AN ASS, having put on the Lion's skin, roamed about in the forest and amused himself by frightening all the foolish animals he met in his wanderings. At last coming upon a Fox, he tried to frighten him also, but the Fox no sooner heard the sound of his voice than he exclaimed, "I might possibly have been frightened myself, if I had not heard your bray."

The Sparrow and the Hare

A HARE pounced upon by an eagle sobbed very much and uttered cries like a child. A Sparrow upbraided her and said, "Where now is thy remarkable swiftness of foot? Why were your feet so slow?" While the Sparrow was thus speaking, a hawk suddenly seized him and killed him. The Hare was comforted in her death, and expiring said, "Ah! you who so lately, when you supposed yourself safe, exulted over my calamity, have now reason to deplore a similar misfortune."

The Flea and the Ox

A FLEA thus questioned an Ox: "What ails you, that being so huge and strong, you submit to the wrongs you receive from men and slave for them day by day, while I, being so small a creature, mercilessly feed on their flesh and drink their blood without stint?" The Ox replied: "I do not wish to be ungrateful, for I am loved and well cared for by men, and they often pat my head and shoulders." "Woe's me!" said the Flea; "this very patting which you like, whenever it happens to me, brings with it my inevitable destruction."

The Goods and the Ills

ALL the *Goods* were once driven out by the *Ills* from that common share which they each had in the affairs of mankind; for the *Ills* by reason of their numbers had prevailed to possess the earth.

The *Goods* wafted themselves to heaven and asked for a right-eous vengeance on their persecutors. They entreated Jupiter that they might no longer be associated with the *Ills,* as they had nothing in common and could not live together, but were en-gaged in unceasing warfare; and that an indissoluble law might be laid down for their future protection. Jupiter granted their request and decreed that henceforth the *Ills* should visit the earth in company with each other, but that the *Goods* should one by one enter the habitations of men. Hence it arises that *Ills* abound, for they come not one by one, but in troops, and by no means singly: while the *Goods* proceed from Jupiter, and are given, not alike to all, but singly, and separately; and one by one to those who are able to discern them.

The Dove and the Crow

A DOVE shut up in a cage was boasting of the large number of young ones which she had hatched. A Crow hearing her, said: "My good friend, cease from this unseasonable boasting. The larger the number of your family, the greater your cause of sor-row, in seeing them shut up in this prison-house."

Mercury and the Workmen

A WORKMAN, felling wood by the side of a river, let his axe drop by accident into a deep pool. Being thus deprived of the means of his livelihood, he sat down on the bank and lamented his hard fate. Mercury appeared and demanded the cause of his tears. After he told him his misfortune, Mercury plunged into the stream, and, bringing up a golden axe, inquired if that were the one he had lost. On his saying that it was not his, Mercury disappeared beneath the water a second time, returned with a silver axe in his hand, and again asked the Workman if it were his. When the Workman said it was not, he dived into the pool for the third time and brought up the axe that had been lost. The Workman claimed it and expressed his joy at its recovery. Mercury, pleased with his honesty, gave him the golden and silver axes in addition to his own.

The Workman, on his return to his house, related to his companions all that had happened. One of them at once resolved to try and secure the same good fortune for himself. He ran to the river and threw his axe on purpose into the pool at the same place, and sat down on the bank to weep. Mercury appeared to him just as he hoped he would; and having learned the cause of his grief, plunged into the stream and brought up a golden axe, inquiring if he had lost it. The Workman seized it greedily, and declared that truly it was the very same axe that he had lost. Mercury, displeased at his knavery, not only took away the golden axe, but refused to recover for him the axe he had thrown into the pool.

The Eagle and the Jackdaw

AN EAGLE, flying down from his perch on a lofty rock, seized upon a lamb and carried him aloft in his talons. A Jackdaw, who witnessed the capture of the lamb, was stirred with envy and determined to emulate the strength and flight of the Eagle. He flew around with a great whirr of his wings and settled upon a large ram, with the intention of carrying him off, but his claws became entangled in the ram's fleece and he was not able to release himself, although he fluttered with his feathers as much as he could. The shepherd, seeing what had happened, ran up and caught him. He at once clipped the Jackdaw's wings, and

taking him home at night, gave him to his children. On their saying, "Father, what kind of bird is it?" he replied, "To my certain
knowledge he is a Daw; but he would like you to think an
Eagle."

The Fox and the Crane

A FOX invited a Crane to supper and provided nothing for his
entertainment but some soup made of pulse, which was poured
out into a broad flat stone dish. The soup fell out of the long
bill of the Crane at every mouthful, and his vexation at not being able to eat afforded the Fox much amusement. The Crane,
in his turn, asked the Fox to sup with him, and set before her a
flagon with a long narrow mouth, so that he could easily insert
his neck and enjoy its contents at his leisure. The Fox, unable
even to taste it, met with a fitting requital, after the fashion of
her own hospitality.

Jupiter, Neptune, Minerva, and Momus

ACCORDING to an ancient legend, the first man was made by
Jupiter, the first bull by Neptune, and the first house by Minerva.
On the completion of their labors, a dispute arose as to which
had made the most perfect work. They agreed to appoint Momus
as judge, and to abide by his decision. Momus, however, being
very envious of the handicraft of each, found fault with all. He
first blamed the work of Neptune because he had not made the
horns of the bull below his eyes, so he might better see where
to strike. He then condemned the work of Jupiter, because he
had not placed the heart of man on the outside, that everyone
might read the thoughts of the evil disposed and take precau-
tions against the intended mischief. And, lastly, he inveighed
against Minerva because she had not contrived iron wheels in
the foundation of her house, so its inhabitants might more easily remove if a neighbor proved unpleasant. Jupiter, indignant at
such inveterate faultfinding, drove him from his office of
judge, and expelled him from the mansions of Olympus.

The Eagle and the Fox

AN EAGLE and a Fox formed an intimate friendship and decided to live near each other. The Eagle built her nest in the
branches of a tall tree, while the Fox crept into the underwood
and there produced her young. Not long after they had agreed
upon this plan, the Eagle, being in want of provision for her
young ones, swooped down while the Fox was out, seized upon
one of the little cubs, and feasted herself and her brood. The
Fox on her return, discovered what had happened, but was
less grieved for the death of her young than for her inability to
avenge them. A just retribution, however, quickly fell upon the

Eagle. While hovering near an altar, on which some villagers were sacrificing a goat, she suddenly seized a piece of the flesh, and carried it, along with a burning cinder, to her nest. A strong breeze soon fanned the spark into a flame, and the eaglets, as yet unfledged and helpless, were roasted in their nest and dropped down dead at the bottom of the tree. There, in the sight of the Eagle, the Fox gobbled them up.

The Man and the Satyr

A MAN and a Satyr once drank together in token of a bond of alliance being formed between them. One very cold wintry day, as they talked, the Man put his fingers to his mouth and blew on them. When the Satyr asked the reason for this, he told him that he did it to warm his hands because they were so cold. Later on in the day they sat down to eat, and the food prepared was quite scalding. The Man raised one of the dishes a little towards his mouth and blew in it. When the Satyr again inquired the reason, he said that he did it to cool the meat, which was too hot. "I can no longer consider you as a friend," said the Satyr, "a fellow who with the same breath blows hot and cold."

The Ass and His Purchaser

A MAN wished to purchase an Ass, and agreed with its owner that he should try out the animal before he bought him. He took the Ass home and put him in the straw-yard with his other Asses, upon which the new animal left all the others and at once joined the one that was most idle and the greatest eater of them all. Seeing this, the man put a halter on him and led him back to his owner. On being asked how, in so short a time, he could have made a trial of him, he answered, "I do not need a trial; I know that he will be just the same as the one he chose for his companion."

A man is known by the company he keeps.

The Two Bags

EVERY MAN, according to an ancient legend, is born into the world with two bags suspended from his neck—a small bag in front full of his neighbors' faults, and a large bag behind filled with his own faults. Hence it is that men are quick to see the faults of others, and yet are often blind to their own failings.

The Stag at the Pool

A STAG overpowered by heat came to a spring to drink. Seeing his own shadow reflected in the water, he greatly admired the size and variety of his horns, but felt angry with himself for having such slender and weak feet. While he was thus contemplating himself, a Lion appeared at the pool and crouched to spring upon him. The Stag immediately took to flight, and exerting his utmost speed, as long as the plain was smooth and open kept himself easily at a safe distance from the Lion. But entering a wood he became entangled by his horns, and the Lion quickly came up to him and caught him. When too late, he thus reproached himself: "Woe is me! How I have deceived myself! These feet which would have saved me I despised, and I gloried in these antlers which have proved my destruction."

What is most truly valuable is often underrated.

The Jackdaw and the Fox

A HALF-FAMISHED JACKDAW seated himself on a fig-tree, which had produced some fruit entirely out of season, and waited in the hope that the figs would ripen. A Fox seeing him sitting so long and learning the reason of his doing so, said to him, "You are indeed, sir, sadly deceiving yourself; you are indulging a hope strong enough to cheat you, but which will never reward you with enjoyment."

The Lark Burying Her Father

THE LARK (according to an ancient legend) was created before the earth itself, and when her father died, as there was no earth, she could find no place of burial for him. She let him lie un-interred for five days, and on the sixth day, not knowing what else to do, she buried him in her own head. Hence she obtained her crest, which is popularly said to be her father's grave-hillock.

Youth's first duty is reverence to parents.

The Gnat and the Bull

A GNAT settled on the horn of a Bull, and sat there a long time. Just as he was about to fly off, he made a buzzing noise, and inquired of the Bull if he would like him to go. The Bull replied, "I did not know you had come, and I shall not miss you when you go away."

Some men are of more consequence in their own eyes than in the eyes of their neighbors.

The Bitch and Her Whelps

A BITCH, ready to whelp, earnestly begged a shepherd for a place where she might litter. When her request was granted, she besought permission to rear her puppies in the same spot. The shepherd again consented. But at last the Bitch, protected by the bodyguard of her Whelps, who had now grown up and were able to defend themselves, asserted her exclusive right to the place and would not permit the shepherd to approach.

The Dogs and the Hides

SOME DOGS famished with hunger saw a number of cowhides steeping in a river. Not being able to reach them, they agreed to drink up the river, but it happened that they burst themselves with drinking long before they reached the hides.

Attempt not impossibilities.

The Shepherd and the Sheep

A SHEPHERD driving his Sheep to a wood, saw an oak of unusual size full of acorns, and spreading his cloak under the branches, he climbed up into the tree and shook them down. The Sheep eating the acorns inadvertently frayed and tore the cloak. When the Shepherd came down and saw what was done, he said, "O you most ungrateful creatures! You provide wool to make garments for all other men, but you destroy the clothes of him who feeds you."

The Grasshopper and the Owl

AN OWL, accustomed to feed at night and to sleep during the day, was greatly disturbed by the noise of a Grasshopper and earnestly besought her to stop chirping. The Grasshopper refused to desist, and chirped louder and louder the more the Owl entreated. When she saw that she could get no redress and that her words were despised, the Owl attacked the chatterer by a stratagem. "Since I cannot sleep," she said, "on account of your song which, believe me, is sweet as the lyre of Apollo, I shall indulge myself in drinking some nectar which Pallas lately gave me. If you do not dislike it, come to me and we will drink it together." The Grasshopper, who was thirsty, and pleased with the praise of her voice, eagerly flew up. The Owl came forth from her hollow, seized her, and put her to death.

The Monkey and the Camel

THE BEASTS of the forest gave a splendid entertainment at which the Monkey stood up and danced. Having vastly delighted the assembly, he sat down amidst universal applause. The Camel, envious of the praises bestowed on the Monkey and desiring to divert to himself the favor of the guests, proposed to stand up in his turn and dance for their amusement. He moved about in so utterly ridiculous a manner that the Beasts, in a fit of indignation, set upon him with clubs and drove him out of the assembly.

It is absurd to ape our betters.

The Peasant and the Apple-Tree

A PEASANT had in his garden an Apple-Tree which bore no fruit but only served as a harbor for the sparrows and grasshoppers. He resolved to cut it down, and taking his axe in his hand, made a bold stroke at its roots. The grasshoppers and sparrows entreated him not to cut down the tree that sheltered them, but to spare it, and they would sing to him and lighten his labors.

He paid no attention to their request, but gave the tree a second and a third blow with his axe. When he reached the hollow of the tree, he found a hive full of honey. Having tasted the honeycomb, he threw down his axe, and looking on the tree as sacred, took great care of it.

Self-interest alone moves some men.

The Two Soldiers and the Robber

TWO SOLDIERS traveling together were set upon by a Robber. The one fled away; the other stood his ground and defended himself with his stout right hand. The Robber being slain, the timid companion ran up and drew his sword, and then, throwing back his traveling cloak, said, "I'll at him, and I'll take care he shall learn whom he has attacked." On this, he who had fought with the Robber made answer, "I only wish that you had helped me just now, even if it had been only with those words, for I should have been the more encouraged, believing them to be true; but now put up your sword in its sheath and hold your equally useless tongue, till you can deceive others who do not know you. I, indeed, who have experienced with what speed you run away, know right well that no dependence can be placed on your valor."

The Trees Under the Protection of the Gods

THE GODS, according to an ancient legend, made choice of certain trees to be under their special protection. Jupiter chose the oak, Venus the myrtle, Apollo the laurel, Cybele the pine, and Hercules the poplar. Minerva, wondering why they had preferred trees not yielding fruit, inquired the reason for their choice. Jupiter replied, "It is lest we should seem to covet the honor for the fruit." But said Minerva, "Let anyone say what he will, the olive is more dear to me on account of its fruit." Then said Jupiter, "My daughter, you are rightly called wise; for unless what we do is useful, the glory of it is vain."

The Mother and the Wolf

A FAMISHED WOLF was prowling about in the morning in search of food. As he passed the door of a cottage built in the forest, he heard a Mother say to her child, "Be quiet, or I will throw you out of the window, and the Wolf shall eat you." The Wolf sat all day waiting at the door. In the evening he heard the same woman fondling her child and saying: "You are quiet now, and if the Wolf should come, we will kill him." The Wolf, hearing these words, went home, gasping with cold and hunger. When he reached his den, Mistress Wolf inquired of him why he returned wearied and supperless, so contrary to his wont. He replied: "Why, forsooth!—because I gave credence to the words of a woman!"

The Ass and the Horse

AN ASS besought a Horse to spare him a small portion of his feed. "Yes," said the Horse; "if any remains out of what I am now eating I will give it you for the sake of my own superior dignity, and if you will come when I reach my own stall in the evening, I will give you a little sack full of barley." The Ass replied, "Thank you. But I can't think that you, who refuse me a little matter now, will by and by confer on me a greater benefit."

Truth and the Traveler

A WAYFARING MAN, traveling in the desert, met a woman standing alone and terribly dejected. He inquired of her, "Who art thou?" "My name is Truth," she replied. "And for what cause," he asked, "have you left the city to dwell alone here in the wilderness?" She made answer, "Because in former times, falsehood was with few, but is now with all men."

The Manslayer

A MAN committed a murder, and was pursued by the relations of the man whom he murdered. On his reaching the river Nile he saw a Lion on its bank, and being fearfully afraid, climbed up a tree. He found a serpent in the upper branches of the tree, and again being greatly alarmed, he threw himself into the river, where a crocodile caught him and ate him. Thus the earth, the air, and the water alike refused shelter to a murderer.

The Lion and the Fox

A FOX entered into partnership with a Lion on the pretense of becoming his servant. Each undertook his proper duty in accordance with his own nature and powers. The Fox discovered and pointed out the prey; the Lion sprang on it and seized it. The Fox soon became jealous of the Lion carrying off the Lion's share, and said that he would no longer find out the prey, but would capture it on his own account. The next day he attempted to snatch a lamb from the fold, but he himself fell prey to the huntsmen and hounds.

The Lion and the Eagle

AN EAGLE stayed his flight and entreated a Lion to make an alliance with him to their mutual advantage. The Lion replied, "I have no objection, but you must excuse me for requiring you to find surety for your good faith, for how can I trust anyone as a friend who is able to fly away from his bargain whenever he pleases?"

Try before you trust.

The Hen and the Swallow

A HEN finding the eggs of a viper and carefully keeping them warm, nourished them into life. A Swallow, observing what she had done, said, "You silly creature! why have you hatched these vipers which, when they shall have grown, will inflict injury on all, beginning with yourself?"

The Buffoon and the Countryman

A RICH NOBLEMAN once opened the theaters without charge to the people, and gave a public notice that he would handsomely reward any person who invented a new amusement for the occasion. Various public performers contended for the prize. Among them came a Buffoon well known among the populace for his jokes, and said that he had a kind of entertainment which had never been brought out on any stage before. This report being spread about made a great stir, and the theater was crowded in every part. The Buffoon appeared alone upon the

platform, without any apparatus or confederates, and the very sense of expectation caused an intense silence. He suddenly bent his head towards his bosom and imitated the squeaking of a little pig so admirably with his voice that the audience declared he had a porker under his cloak, and demanded that it should be shaken out. When that was done and nothing was found, they cheered the actor, and loaded him with the loudest applause. A Countryman in the crowd, observing all that has passed, said, "So help me, Hercules, he shall not beat me at that trick!" and at once proclaimed that he would do the same thing on the next day, though in a much more natural way. On the morrow a still larger crowd assembled in the theater, but now partiality for their favorite actor very generally prevailed, and the audience came rather to ridicule the Countryman than to see the spectacle. Both of the performers appeared on the stage. The Buffoon grunted and squeaked away first, and obtained, as on the preceding day, the applause and cheers of the spectators. Next the Countryman commenced, and pretending that he concealed a little pig beneath his clothes (which in truth he did, but not suspected by the audience) contrived to take hold of and to pull his ear causing the pig to squeak. The Crowd, however, cried out with one consent that the Buffoon had given a far more exact imitation, and clamored for the Countryman to be kicked out of the theater. On this the rustic produced the little pig from his cloak and showed by the most positive proof the greatness of their mistake. "Look here," he said, "this shows what sort of judges you are."

The Crow and the Serpent

A CROW in great want of food saw a Serpent asleep in a sunny nook, and flying down, greedily seized him. The Serpent, turning about, bit the Crow with a mortal wound. In the agony of death, the bird exclaimed: "O unhappy me! who have found in that which I deemed a happy windfall the source of my destruction."

The Hunter and the Horseman

A CERTAIN HUNTER, having snared a hare, placed it upon his shoulders and set out homewards. On his way he met a man on horseback who begged the hare of him, under the pretense of purchasing it. However, when the Horseman got the hare, he rode off as fast as he could. The Hunter ran after him, as if he was sure of overtaking him, but the Horseman increased more and more the distance between them. The Hunter, sorely against his will, called out to him and said, "Get along with you! for I will now make you a present of the hare."

The King's Son and the Painted Lion

A KING, whose only son was fond of martial exercises, had a dream in which he was warned that his son would be killed by a lion. Afraid the dream should prove true, he built for his son a pleasant palace and adorned its walls for his amusement with all kinds of life-sized animals, among which was the picture of a lion. When the young Prince saw this, his grief at being thus confined burst out afresh, and, standing near the lion, he said: "O you most detestable of animals! through a lying dream of my father's, which he saw in his sleep, I am shut up on your account in this palace as if I had been a girl: what shall I now do to you?" With these words he stretched out his hands toward a thorn-tree, meaning to cut a stick from its branches so that he might beat the lion. But one of the tree's prickles pierced his finger and caused great pain and inflammation, so that the young Prince fell down in a fainting fit. A violent fever suddenly set in, from which he died not many days later.

We had better bear our troubles bravely than try to escape them.

The Cat and Venus

A CAT fell in love with a handsome young man, and entreated Venus to change her into the form of a woman. Venus consented to her request and transformed her into a beautiful damsel, so that the youth saw her and loved her, and took her home as his bride. While the two were reclining in their chamber, Venus wishing to discover if the Cat in her change of shape had also altered her habits of life, let down a mouse in the middle of the room. The Cat, quite forgetting her present condition, started up from the couch and pursued the mouse, wishing to eat it. Venus was much disappointed and again caused her to return to her former shape.

Nature exceeds nurture.

The She-Goats and Their Beards

THE SHE-GOATS having obtained a beard by request to Jupiter, the He-Goats were sorely displeased and made complaint that the females equaled them in dignity. "Allow them," said Jupiter, "to enjoy an empty honor and to assume the badge of your nobler sex, so long as they are not your equals in strength or courage."

It matters little if those who are inferior to us in merit should be like us in outside appearances.

The Camel and the Arab

AN ARAB CAMEL-DRIVER, after completing the loading of his Camel, asked him which he would like best, to go up hill or down. The poor beast replied, not without a touch of reason: "Why do you ask me? Is it that the level way through the desert is closed?"

The Miller, His Son, and Their Ass

A MILLER and his son were driving their Ass to a neighboring fair to sell him. They had not gone far when they met with a troop of women collected round a well, talking and laughing. "Look there," cried one of them, "did you ever see such fellows, to be trudging along the road on foot when they might ride?" The old man hearing this, quickly made his son mount the Ass, and continued to walk along merrily by his side. Presently they came up to a group of old men in earnest debate. "There," said one of them, "it proves what I was a-saying. What respect is shown to old age in these days? Do you see that idle lad riding while his old father has to walk? Get down, you young scapegrace, and let the old man rest his weary limbs." Upon this the old man made his son dismount, and got up himself. In this manner they had not proceeded far when they met a company of women and children: "Why, you lazy old fellow," cried several tongues at once, "how can you ride upon the beast, while that poor little lad there can hardly keep pace by the side of you?" The good-natured Miller immediately took up his son behind him. They had now almost reached the town.

"Pray, honest friend," said a citizen, "is that Ass your own?" "Yes," replied the old man. "O, one would not have thought so," said the other, "by the way you load him. Why, you two fellows are better able to carry the poor beast than he you." "Anything to please you," said the old man; "we can but try." So, alighting with his son, they tied the legs of the Ass together and with the help of a pole endeavored to carry him on their shoulders over a bridge near the entrance to the town. This entertaining sight brought the people in crowds to laugh at it, till the Ass, not liking the noise nor the strange handling that he was subject to, broke the cords that bound him and, tumbling off the pole, fell into the river. Upon this, the old man, vexed and ashamed, made the best of his way home again, convinced that by endeavoring to please everybody he had pleased nobody, and lost his Ass in the bargain.

The Crow and the Sheep

A TROUBLESOME CROW seated herself on the back of a Sheep. The Sheep, much against his will, carried her backward and forward for a long time, and at last said, "If you had treated a dog in this way, you would have had your deserts from his sharp teeth." To this the Crow replied, "I despise the weak and yield to the strong. I know whom I may bully and whom I must flatter; and I thus prolong my life to a good old age."

The Fox and the Bramble

A FOX was mounting a hedge when he lost his footing and caught hold of a Bramble to save himself. Having pricked and grievously torn the soles of his feet, he accused the Bramble because, when he had fled to her for assistance, she had used him worse than the hedge itself. The Bramble, interrupting him, said, "But you really must have been out of your senses to fasten yourself on me, who am myself always accustomed to fasten upon others."

The Wolf and the Lion

A WOLF, having stolen a lamb from a fold, was carrying him off to his lair. A Lion met him in the path, and seizing the lamb, took it from him. Standing at a safe distance, the Wolf exclaimed, "You have unrighteously taken that which was mine from me!" To which the Lion jeeringly replied, "It was righteously yours, eh? The gift of a friend?"

The Dog and the Oyster

A DOG, used to eating eggs, saw an Oyster and, opening his mouth to its widest extent, swallowed it down with the utmost relish, supposing it to be an egg. Soon afterwards suffering great pain in his stomach, he said, "I deserve all this torment, for my folly in thinking that everything round must be an egg."

They who act without sufficient thought, will often fall into unsuspected danger.

The Ant and the Dove

AN ANT went to the bank of a river to quench its thirst, and being carried away by the rush of the stream, was on the point of drowning. A Dove sitting on a tree overhanging the water plucked a leaf and let it fall into the stream close to her. The Ant climbed onto it and floated in safety to the bank. Shortly afterwards a birdcatcher came and stood under the tree, and laid his lime-twigs for the Dove, which sat in the branches. The Ant, perceiving his design, stung him in the foot. In pain the birdcatcher threw down the twigs, and the noise made the Dove take wing.

The Partridge and the Fowler

A FOWLER caught a Partridge and was about to kill it. The Partridge earnestly begged him to spare his life, saying, "Pray, master, permit me to live and I will entice many Partridges to you in recompense for your mercy to me." The Fowler replied, "I shall now with less scruple take your life, because you are willing to save it at the cost of betraying your friends and relations."

The Flea and the Man

A MAN, very much annoyed with a Flea, caught him at last, and said, "Who are you who dare to feed on my limbs, and to cost me so much trouble in catching you?" The Flea replied, "O my dear sir, pray spare my life, and destroy me not, for I cannot possibly do you much harm." The Man, laughing, replied, "Now you shall certainly die by mine own hands, for no evil, whether it be small or large, ought to be tolerated."

The Thieves and the Cock

SOME THIEVES broke into a house and found nothing but a Cock, whom they stole, and got off as fast as they could. Upon arriving at home they prepared to kill the Cock, who thus pleaded for his life: "Pray spare me; I am very serviceable to men. I wake them up in the night to their work." "That is the very reason why we must the more kill you," they replied; "for when you wake your neighbors, you entirely put an end to our business."

The safeguards of virtue are hateful to those with evil intentions.

The Dog and the Cook

A RICH MAN gave a great feast, to which he invited many friends and acquaintances. His Dog availed himself of the occasion to invite a stranger Dog, a friend of his, saying, "My master gives a feast, and there is always much food remaining; come and sup with me tonight." The Dog thus invited went at the hour appointed, and seeing the preparations for so grand an entertainment, said in the joy of his heart, "How glad I am that I came! I do not often get such a chance as this. I will take care and eat enough to last me both today and tomorrow." While he was congratulating himself and wagging his tail to convey his pleasure to his friend, the Cook saw him moving about among his dishes and, seizing him by his fore and hind paws, bundled him without ceremony out of the window. He fell with force upon the ground and limped away, howling dreadfully. His yelling soon attracted other street dogs, who came up to him and inquired how he had enjoyed his supper. He replied, "Why, to tell you the truth, I drank so much wine that I remember nothing. I do not know how I got out of the house."

The Travelers and the Plane-Tree

TWO TRAVELERS, worn out by the heat of the summer's sun, laid themselves down at noon under the widespreading branches of a Plane-Tree. As they rested under its shade, one of the Travelers said to the other, "What a singularly useless tree is the Plane! It bears no fruit, and is not of the least service to man." The Plane-Tree, interrupting him, said, "You ungrateful fellows! Do you, while receiving benefits from me and resting under my shade, dare to describe me as useless, and unprofitable?"

Some men underrate their best blessings.

The Hares and the Frogs

THE HARES, oppressed by their own exceeding timidity and weary of the perpetual alarm to which they were exposed, with one accord determined to put an end to themselves and their troubles by jumping from a lofty precipice into a deep lake below. As they scampered off in large numbers to carry out their resolve, the Frogs lying on the banks of the lake heard the noise of their feet and rushed helter-skelter to the deep water for safety. On seeing the rapid disappearance of the Frogs, one of the Hares cried out to his companions: "Stay, my friends, do not do as you intended; for you now see that there are creatures who are still more timid than ourselves."

The Lion, Jupiter, and the Elephant

THE LION wearied Jupiter with his frequent complaints. "It is true, O Jupiter!" he said, "that I am gigantic in strength, handsome in shape, and powerful in attack. I have jaws well provided with teeth, and feet furnished with claws, and I lord it over all the beasts of the forest, and what a disgrace it is, that being such as I am, I should be frightened by the crowing of a cock." Jupiter replied, "Why do you blame me without a cause? I have given you all the attributes which I possess myself, and your courage never fails you except in this one instance." On hearing this the Lion groaned and lamented very much and, reproaching himself with his cowardice, wished that he might die. As these thoughts passed through his mind, he met an Elephant and came close to hold a conversation with him. After a time he observed that the Elephant shook his ears very often, and he inquired what was the matter and why his ears moved with such a tremor every now and then. Just at that moment a Gnat settled on the head of the Elephant, and he replied, "Do you see that little buzzing insect? If it enters my ear, my fate is sealed. I should die presently." The Lion said, "Well, since so huge a beast is afraid of a tiny gnat, I will no more complain, nor wish myself dead. I find myself, even as I am, better off than the Elephant."

The Lamb and the Wolf

A WOLF pursued a Lamb, which fled for refuge to a certain Temple. The Wolf called out to him and said, "The Priest will slay you in sacrifice, if he should catch you." On which the Lamb replied, "It would be better for me to be sacrificed in the Temple than to be eaten by you."

The Rich Man and the Tanner

A RICH MAN lived near a Tanner, and not being able to bear the unpleasant smell of the tan-yard, he pressed his neighbor to go away. The Tanner put off his departure from time to time, saying that he would leave soon. But as he still continued to stay, as time went on, the rich man became accustomed to the smell, and feeling no manner of inconvenience, made no further complaints.

The Shipwrecked Man and the Sea

A SHIPWRECKED MAN, having been cast upon a certain shore, slept after his buffetings with the deep. After a while he awoke, and looking upon the Sea, loaded it with reproaches. He argued that it enticed men with the calmness of its looks, but when it had induced them to plow its waters, it grew rough and destroyed them. The Sea, assuming the form of a woman, replied to him: "Blame not me, my good sir, but the winds, for I am by my own nature as calm and firm even as this earth; but the winds suddenly falling on me create these waves, and lash me into fury."

The Mules and the Robbers

TWO MULES well-laden with packs were trudging along. One carried panniers filled with money, the other sacks weighted with grain. The Mule carrying the treasure walked with head erect, as if conscious of the value of his burden, and tossed up and down the clear-toned bells fastened to his neck. His companion followed with quiet and easy step. All of a sudden Robbers rushed upon them from their hiding-places, and in the scuffle with their owners, wounded with a sword the Mule carrying the treasure, which they greedily seized while taking no notice of the grain. The Mule which had been robbed and wounded bewailed his misfortunes. The other replied, "I am indeed glad that I was thought so little of, for I have lost nothing, nor am I hurt with any wound."

The Viper and the File

A VIPER, entering the workshop of a smith, sought from the tools the means of satisfying his hunger. He more particularly addressed himself to a File, and asked of him the favor of a meal. The File replied, "You must indeed be a simple-minded fellow if you expect to get anything from me, who am accustomed to take from everyone, and never to give anything in return."

The Lion and the Shepherd

A LION, roaming through a forest, trod upon a thorn. Soon afterward he came up to a Shepherd and fawned upon him, wagging his tail as if to say, "I am a suppliant, and seek your aid." The

Shepherd boldly examined the beast, discovered the thorn, and placing his paw upon his lap, pulled it out; thus relieved of his pain, the Lion returned into the forest. Some time after, the Shepherd, being imprisoned on a false accusation, was condemned "to be cast to the Lions" as the punishment for his imputed crime. But when the Lion was released from his cage, he recognized the Shepherd as the man who healed him, and instead of attacking him, approached and placed his foot upon his lap. The King, as soon as he heard the tale, ordered the Lion to be set free again in the forest, and the Shepherd to be pardoned and restored to his friends.

The Camel and Jupiter

THE CAMEL, when he saw the Bull adorned with horns, envied him and wished that he himself could obtain the same honors. He went to Jupiter, and besought him to give him horns. Jupiter, vexed at his request because he was not satisfied with his size and strength of body, and desired yet more, not only refused to give him horns, but even deprived him of a portion of his ears.

The Panther and the Shepherds

A PANTHER, by some mischance, fell into a pit. The Shepherds discovered him, and some threw sticks at him and pelted him with stones, while others, moved with compassion towards one about to die even though no one should hurt him, threw in some food to prolong his life. At night they returned home, not dreaming of any danger, but supposing that on the morrow they would find him dead. The Panther, however, when he had recruited his feeble strength, freed himself with a sudden bound from the pit, and hastened to his den with rapid steps. After a few days he came forth and slaughtered the cattle, and, killing the Shepherds who had attacked him, raged with angry fury. Then they who had spared his life, fearing for their safety, surrendered to him their flocks and begged only for their lives. To them the Panther made this reply: "I remember alike those who sought my life with stones, and those who gave me food—lay aside, therefore, your fears. I return as an enemy only to those who injured me."

The Ass and the Charger

AN ASS congratulated a Horse on being so ungrudgingly and carefully provided for, while he himself had scarcely enough to eat and not even that without hard work. But when war broke out, a heavily armed soldier mounted the Horse, and riding him to the charge, rushed into the very midst of the enemy. The Horse was wounded and fell dead on the battlefield. Then the Ass, seeing all these things, changed his mind, and commiserated the Horse.

The Eagle and His Captor

AN EAGLE was once captured by a man, who immediately clipped his wings and put him into his poultry-yard with the other birds, at which treatment the Eagle was weighed down with grief. Later, another neighbor purchased him and allowed his feathers to grow again. The Eagle took flight, and pouncing upon a hare, brought it at once as an offering to his benefactor. A Fox, seeing this, exclaimed, "Do not cultivate the favor of this man, but of your former owner, lest he should again hunt for you and deprive you a second time of your wings."

The Bald Man and the Fly

A FLY bit the bare head of a Bald Man who, endeavoring to destroy it, gave himself a heavy slap. Escaping, the Fly said mockingly, "You who have wished to revenge, even with death, the prick of a tiny insect, see what you have done to yourself to add insult to injury?" The Bald Man replied, "I can easily make peace with myself, because I know there was no intention to hurt. But you, an ill-favored and contemptible insect who delights in sucking human blood, I wish that I could have killed you even if I had incurred a heavier penalty."

The Olive-Tree and the Fig-Tree

THE OLIVE-TREE ridiculed the Fig-Tree because, while she was green all the year round, the Fig-Tree changed its leaves with the seasons. A shower of snow fell upon them, and, finding the Olive full of foliage, it settled upon its branches and broke them down with its weight, at once despoiling it of its beauty and killing the tree. But finding the Fig-Tree denuded of leaves, the snow fell through to the ground, and did not injure it at all.

The Eagle and the Kite

AN EAGLE, overwhelmed with sorrow, sat upon the branches of a tree in company with a Kite. "Why," said the Kite, "do I see you with such a rueful look?" "I seek," she replied, "a mate suitable for me, and am not able to find one." "Take me," returned the Kite, "I am much stronger than you are." "Why, are you able to secure the means of living by your plunder?" "Well, I have often caught and carried away an ostrich in my talons." The Eagle, persuaded by these words, accepted him as her mate. Shortly after the nuptials, the Eagle said, "Fly off and bring me back the ostrich you promised me." The Kite, soaring aloft into the air, brought back the shabbiest possible mouse, stinking from the length of time it had lain about the fields. "Is this," said the Eagle, "the faithful fulfillment of your promise to me?" The Kite replied, "That I might attain your royal hand, there is nothing that I would not have promised, however much I knew that I must fail in the performance."

The Ass and His Driver

AN ASS, being driven along a high road, suddenly started off and bolted to the brink of a deep precipice. While he was in the act of throwing himself over, his owner seized him by the tail, endeavoring to pull him back. When the Ass persisted in his effort, the man let him go and said, "Conquer, but conquer to your cost."

The Thrush and the Fowler

A THRUSH was feeding on a myrtle-tree and did not move from it because its berries were so delicious. A Fowler observed her staying so long in one spot, and having well bird-limed his reeds, caught her. The Thrush, being at the point of death, exclaimed, "O foolish creature that I am! For the sake of a little pleasant food I have deprived myself of my life."

The Rose and the Amaranth

AN AMARANTH planted in a garden near a Rose-Tree, thus addressed it: "What a lovely flower is the Rose, a favorite alike with Gods and with men. I envy you your beauty and your perfume." The Rose replied, "I indeed, dear Amaranth, flourish but for a brief season! If no cruel hand pluck me from my stem, yet I must perish by an early doom. But thou art *immortal* and dost never fade, but bloomest for ever in renewed youth."

The Frogs' Complaint Against the Sun

ONCE UPON A TIME, when the Sun announced his intention to take a wife, the Frogs lifted up their voices in clamor to the sky. Jupiter, disturbed by the noise of their croaking, inquired the cause of their complaint. One of them said, "The Sun, now while he is single, parches up the marsh, and compels us to die miserably in our arid homes. What will be our future condition if he should beget other suns?"

APPENDIX

LIFE OF ÆSOP

THE LIFE and History of Æsop is involved, like that of Homer, the most famous of Greek poets, in much obscurity. Sardis, the capital of Lydia; Samos, a Greek island; Mesembria, an ancient colony in Thrace; and Cotiæum, the chief city of a province of Phrygia, contend for the distinction of being the birthplace of Æsop. Although the honour thus claimed cannot be definitely assigned to any one of these places, yet there are a few incidents now generally accepted by scholars as established facts, relating to the birth, life, and death of Æsop. He is, by an almost universal consent, allowed to have been born about the year 620 B.C., and to have been by birth a slave. He was owned by two masters in succession, both inhabitants of Samos, Xanthus and Jadmon, the latter of whom gave him his liberty as a reward for his learning and wit. One of the privileges of a freedman in the ancient republics of Greece, was the permission to take an active interest in public affairs; and Æsop, like the philosophers Phædo, Menippus, and Epictetus, in later times, raised himself from the indignity of a servile condition to a position of high renown. In his desire alike to instruct and to be instructed, he travelled through many countries, and among others came to Sardis, the capital of the famous king of Lydia, the great patron, in that day, of learning and of learned men. He met at the court of Crœsus with Solon, Thales, and other sages, and is related so to have pleased his royal master, by the part he took in the conversations held with these philosophers, that he applied to him an expression which has since passed into a proverb, "μᾶλλον ὁ Φρύξ." "The Phrygian has spoken better than all."

On the invitation of Crœsus he fixed his residence at Sardis, and was employed by that monarch in various difficult and delicate affairs of State. In his discharge of these commissions he visited the different petty republics of Greece. At one time he is found in Corinth, and at another in Athens, endeavouring, by the narration of some of his wise fables, to reconcile the inhabitants of those cities to the administration of their respective rulers Periander and Pisistratus. One of these ambassadorial missions, undertaken at the command of Crœsus, was the occasion of his death. Having been sent to Delphi with a large sum of gold for distribution among the citizens, he was so provoked at their covetousness that he refused to divide the money, and sent it back to his master. The Delphians, enraged at this treatment, accused him of impiety, and, in spite of his sacred character as ambassador, executed him as a public criminal. This cruel death of Æsop was not unavenged. The citizens of Delphi were visited with a series of calamities, until they made a public reparation of their crime; and, "The blood of Æsop" became a well-known adage, bearing witness to the truth that deeds of wrong would not pass unpunished. Neither did the great fabulist lack posthumous honours; for a statue was erected to his memory at Athens, the work of Lysippus, one of the most famous of Greek sculptors. Phædrus thus immortalizes the event:—

> Æsopo ingentem statuam posuere Attici,
> Servumque collocarunt æternâ in basi:
> Patere honoris scirent ut cuncti viam;
> Nec generi tribui sed virtuti gloriam.

These few facts are all that can be relied on with any degree of certainty, in reference to the birth, life, and death of Æsop. They were first brought to light, after a patient search and diligent perusal of ancient authors, by a Frenchman, M. Claude Gaspard Bachet de Mezeriac, who declined the honour of being tutor to Louis XIII of France, from his desire to devote himself exclusively to literature. He published his Life of Æsop, Anno Domini 1632. The later investigations of a host of English and German scholars have added very little to the facts given by M. Mezeriac. The substantial truth of his statements has been confirmed by later criticism and inquiry. It remains to state, that prior to this publication of M. Mezeriac, the life of Æsop was from the pen of Maximus Planudes, a monk of Constantinople, who was sent on an embassy to Venice by the Byzantine Emperor Andronicus the elder, and who wrote in the early part of the fourteenth century. His life was prefixed to all the early editions of these fables, and was republished as late as 1727 by Archdeacon Croxall as the introduction to his edition of Æsop. This life by Planudes contains, however, so small an amount of truth, and is so full of absurd pictures of the grotesque deformity of Æsop, of wondrous apocryphal stories, of lying legends, and gross anachronisms, that it is now universally condemned as false, puerile, and unauthentic.[1] It is given up in the present day, by general consent, as unworthy of the slightest credit.

G.F.T.

---

[1] M. Bayle thus characterises this Life of Æsop by Planudes, "Tous les habiles gens conviennent que c'est un roman, et que les absurdités grossières qui l'on y trouve le rendent indigne de toute créance."—*Dictionnaire Historique*. Art. *Esope*.

INDEX OF TITLES